CITIZEN

15

LESSONS THAT BRING BIOLOGY TO LIFE, 6-12

SCIENCE

Edited by

NANCY M. TRAUTMANN

JENNIFER FEE

TERRY M. TOMASEK

NANCYLEE R. BERGEY

NSTApress

National Science Teachers Association

Arlington, Virginia

National Science Teachers Association

Claire Reinburg, Director
Andrew Cooke, Senior Editor
Amanda O'Brien, Associate Editor
Wendy Rubin, Associate Editor
Amy America, Book Acquisitions Coordinator

ART AND DESIGN
Will Thomas Jr., Director
Joe Butera, Senior Graphic Designer, cover and
    interior design

PRINTING AND PRODUCTION
Catherine Lorrain, Director

NATIONAL SCIENCE TEACHERS ASSOCIATION
David L. Evans, Executive Director
David Beacom, Publisher

1840 Wilson Blvd., Arlington, VA 22201
www.nsta.org/store
For customer service inquiries, please call 800-277-5300.

Copyright © 2013 by the National Science Teachers Association.
All rights reserved. Printed in the United States of America.
16 15 14 13   4 3 2 1

Library of Congress Cataloging-in-Publication Data

Citizen science: 15 lessons that bring biology to life, 6–12 / edited by Nancy M. Trautmann, Jennifer Fee, Terry M. Tomasek, and NancyLee R. Bergey.
    pages cm
  Includes index.
  ISBN 978-1-936959-08-2
  1. Biology—Study and teaching (Secondary)—Activity programs. 2. Biology—Research—Citizen participation. I. Trautmann, Nancy M., editor of compilation.
  QH316.4.C58 2013
  570.71—dc23
                    2013020455

This material is based upon work supported by the National Science Foundation under a number of grants. Any opinions, findings, and conclusions or recommendations expressed in this material are those of the author(s) and do not necessarily reflect the views of the National Science Foundation.

CONTENTS

CONTENTS

L E S S O

N S

_____

Acknowledgments

This book was inspired by conversations at an NSTA National Conference among educators involved in citizen science. It represents extensive collaboration between curriculum specialists, science teachers, and scientists, some of whom are named as lesson authors and others of whom contributed vital reviews of lesson strategies and scientific content. The lessons were selected through a competition that yielded more high-quality lessons than we were able to include, and we extend deep thanks to all who participated. Jennifer Goforth served as our indispensible research and writing intern, and Irka Elsevier as a key editorial advisor. Many of the citizen science and education efforts represented in this book have been supported by grants from the National Science Foundation.

About the Editors

Nancy M. Trautmann is Director of Education at the Cornell Lab of Ornithology, where she leads a team that creates educational resources and experiences aiming to spark curiosity, build science skills, and inspire conservation action (*www.birds.cornell.edu/education*). She is lead author in the Cornell Scientific Inquiry Series published by NSTA Press, with titles including *Assessing Toxic Risk, Decay and Renewal, Invasion Ecology*, and *Watershed Dynamics*. She holds a doctorate in computer supported collaborative learning, and her academic interests center on engaging students in scientific research and citizen science, supporting effective teacher professional development, and exploring the potential of educational technology in supporting student collaboration and project-based learning.

Jennifer Fee is the Manager of K–12 Programs at the Cornell Lab of Ornithology. She is the lead author of the BirdSleuth curriculum (*www.birdsleuth.org*), with modules including Most Wanted Birds, Afterschool Investigators: Nature Detectives, and Investigating Evidence. She is interested in sharing citizen science and inquiry-based teaching with educators, particularly through curricula and online and in-person professional development workshops. She is a graduate from Truman State University (BS in Biology) and Illinois State University (MS in Behavior, Ecology, Evolution, and Systematics).

Terry M. Tomasek is an Associate Professor in the Department of Teacher Education at Elon University (North Carolina) where she is the Secondary Science Program Coordinator and teaches courses in Educational Assessment, Principles of Learning and Teaching, and General Studies. She is broadly interested in herpetology and engaging high school students in scientific investigations. She received her PhD in Science Education from the University of North Carolina at Greensboro, and her academic interests center on engaged learning and supporting effective teacher professional development.

NancyLee Rodenberg Bergey teaches science in elementary and middle schools as Associate Director of Teacher Education at the Graduate School of Education at the University of Pennsylvania. Before coming to Penn full-time, NancyLee taught, primarily science, for 29 years in schools that spanned the public/independent, urban/suburban, and elementary/middle school range. She also served as an adjunct professor at several colleges as well as writing for and teaching in a number of museums. Her current work focuses on improving science teaching in urban schools through the involvement of undergraduate science students and a focus on urban environmental issues.

Preface
Why Citizen Science?

Observing the life cycle of monarch butterflies and following their remarkable migratory journeys between Canada, the United States, and Mexico...

Tracking climate change by recording the dates of first leaf, flower, and fruit of local trees, shrubs, flowers, and grasses...

Discovering which bird species migrate, where they go, and when...

Exploring life cycles and population dynamics of frogs, toads, and other animals in nearby ponds...

Citizen science projects such as those listed above gather data through public collaboration in scientific research. Who are the "citizens" who take part in such efforts? Some are students and others are interested or concerned individuals from all walks of life. Together, professional and volunteer scientists collaborate to investigate biological and environmental trends over regions and timelines far broader than anyone could tackle individually.

For teachers, citizen science offers a way to motivate and inspire students through participation in research that is relevant both locally and globally. Students build meaningful connections to the natural world as they make observations, collect data, and view their findings within the broader scope of the project. When students design and conduct their own investigations, they also build science practice understandings and analytical reasoning skills through their involvement in citizen science.

In this book, we profile several scenarios of middle school classes engaging in citizen science and provide 15 lessons that present specific ways to build citizen science data collection and analysis into your science teaching. The lessons are organized around the 5E Instructional Model to progress from engagement and exploration through explanation, elaboration, and evaluation, and they engage students in the full range of science practices delineated in the *Next Generation Science Standards (NGSS)*.

We invite you to dig in and become part of the exciting and rapidly growing citizen science movement. Your students will not only learn science, they will be scientists, and their projects will bring biological and environmental science to life in your classes. What better way to fulfill the *NGSS* mandate to couple science practice with content and give students a real-world context in which to apply what they are learning?

Chapter 1
What Is Citizen Science?

Citizen science refers to efforts in which volunteers partner with professional scientists to collect or analyze data. Citizen scientists are individuals in all walks of life—students, the general public, and even professional scientists. As described by a blogger, "The citizen in citizen science is a person who recognizes and studies the local ecology that they themselves are a part of … The citizen science projects that I participate in are… inquiries into my world, the world that I'm a citizen of" (Miller 2008). The word *citizen* conveys the idea that anybody can participate in the collective enterprise of science, just as all citizens in a democracy are invited to vote and otherwise collaborate in building their government (Cooper 2012a).

The efforts of citizen scientists range from searching for rare species to classifying the shapes of galaxies. In one way or another, all involve public collaboration in scientific research. Cornell University scientist Caren Cooper compares citizen science with stone soup: "Soon curiosity wins over the initial distrust and skepticism of impoverished villagers as each, in turn, are enticed to add a vegetable or a spice. Through cooperation and sharing, the entire village feasts on delicious, nutritious soup (Cooper 2012b). She goes on to note, "When my colleagues and I carry out research using citizen science methods, we are like the monks boiling stone soup. Instead of a pot, we have a big blank spreadsheet and curious folk are enticed to each add their observations, ultimately creating a robust database with observations from across a continent." Just as peasants in this folktale collectively create delicious soup with their seemingly insignificant contributions of ingredients, citizen scientists collectively accomplish scientific achievements that would eb impossible by any individual working alone.

One of the longest standing citizen science projects dates back to 1900, when the National Audubon Society launched its annual Christmas Bird Count to involve the public in identifying and counting birds rather than shooting them. Other longstanding projects have involved people in tracking seasonal change, for example by recording the dates on which lake ice melts or particular plant species come into bloom each year in a specified location. In recent years, advances in database and internet capabilities have made it possible for anyone to view and use citizen science data collected across the continent or even around the globe, opening up exciting new possibilities for engaging students in analysis and interpretation of real scientific data sets to which they too can contribute.

Although citizen science extends into astronomy, weather, and a variety of other fields, the projects in this book focus on ecology and natural history. For example:

- Through a network called Hands on the Land, classes inventory terrestrial invertebrates or look for damage to plants caused by ground-level ozone in their school yards or in one of many parks or public lands throughout the country (see Lessons 3 and 10).

- In North and South Carolina, students join with other volunteers to survey amphibians and reptiles and provide data to the Carolina Herp Atlas, which is used by scientists for research and by government agencies in making conservation decisions (see Chapter 6 and Lesson 12).

- Volunteers throughout the United States contribute to climate change research by submitting dates of first leafing, flowering, and fruit ripening of native trees, shrubs, flowers, and grasses in their local area to citizen science projects including Project BudBurst and Nature's Notebook (see Lessons 8 and 9).

Citizen science encompasses a huge range of topics, geographic settings, and strategies. Some projects are confined to a single town or watershed while others are global in scope. Some focus on individual species while others investigate broader taxonomic groups or even entire ecosystems. And some projects are orchestrated by professional scientists while others originate through a grassroots approach.

Most of the citizen science projects represented in this book were organized by professional scientists or organizations interested in collecting data about a particular species or taxonomic group. Using data collected by volunteers, these scientists conduct research over geographic scales beyond what they could cover on their own, in some cases spanning the entire globe! Citizen science also can span time frames longer than the careers of individual scientists, creating data sets that make it possible to track long-term changes in species or ecosystems. Environmental monitoring by citizen scientists creates baseline data that prove useful in times of ecological change, for example in tracking the impacts of events such as volcanic eruptions or oil spills or more gradual changes caused by urbanization or shifting climate (Dickinson et al. 2012). Some projects are hypothesis-driven, collecting data targeted at addressing a specific research question. Others focus on environmental monitoring more generally. Using datasets generated by either type of project, students can look for trends and test hypotheses of their own design.

What Do Citizen Scientists Do?

Citizen science activities vary widely, depending on goals of the project and interests of individual participants. Perhaps the most common activity is data collection. In the Lost Ladybug Project, for example, participants throughout the United States photograph ladybugs and upload digital images to the project website. These efforts make it possible for Cornell University entomologists to track distribution and abundance of ladybug species, including some that are extremely rare and others that are increasing in both abundance and range. In Jellywatch, hosted by the Monterey Bay Aquarium, anyone who sees jellyfish, squid, or related organisms on a beach or in the ocean is invited to submit information and photographs to the project website. Synthesis of these reports will help scientists explore potential causes of jellyfish blooms, examine the effects on ocean ecosystems, and identify consequences of tourism, industry, and fisheries. In Project Squirrel, students and other citizen scientists conduct investigations of squirrel foraging behavior to help scientists determine how squirrels perceive the safety of various foraging locations and test the theory that an animal will cease using a particular foraging patch when the costs of feeding there are perceived to be greater than the benefits (see Lesson 15).

Beyond collecting information on individual species or groups, citizen scientists also monitor environmental conditions such as water quality. In cities and towns throughout the United States, volunteers monitor local streams through the Izaak Walton League of America's "Save Our Streams" (SOS) Program. Students and other participants map physical conditions in a stream and along its banks, conduct chemical tests, and inventory the types and numbers of aquatic invertebrates. Such monitoring goes beyond simple data collection. Trained volunteers also analyze the quality of fish and wildlife habitat and identify sources of existing or potential future degradation.

Although citizen science most commonly involves collecting and submitting data, participants in some projects contribute to scientific discoveries by helping to analyze what would otherwise be unmanageable amounts of data. The Whale.FM project, for example, invites citizen scientists to help marine researchers study the language of whales. Volunteers listen to a sound clip of whale song on the project website and match it with one of several other provided sounds (see Lesson 1). Categorizing the data in this way transforms the previously overwhelming collection of unsorted sound files into a scientifically useful catalogue that has been sorted and tagged. Researchers can more readily use these files to decode the language of whales and better understand what types of sound are made for what purpose.

How Are Citizen Science Data Used?

Through assembling natural history data over previously unimaginable spatial and temporal scales, citizen science is making it possible for researchers to tackle critical questions in ecology and conservation. For example, researchers used data collected by volunteers in the Monarch Larva Monitoring Project to investigate the impacts of land use change and pesticide use on monarch populations over time and to evaluate the risk posed to monarchs by exposure to pollen from genetically modified corn (Oberhauser and Prysby 2008). Data submitted by Journey North participants made it possible for scientists to create the first detailed map of the fall migration flyway of monarchs in eastern North America (Howard and Davis 2009) (Chapter 5 and Lesson 2). Citizen science efforts such as these provide data essential in outlining plans for habitat protection and conservation of monarch butterflies through all stages of their life cycles and migratory ranges.

Similarly, USGS biologists follow population trends and set conservation priorities for amphibians using data generated through volunteer monitoring of frog calls in the North American Amphibian Monitoring Program (see Chapter 6 and Lesson 12). And the wealth of data collected through widespread and long-term bird projects such as the Christmas Bird Count, Project FeederWatch, and eBird allows scientists to track bird migration, accurately map where each North American bird species lives in breeding and nonbreeding seasons, and document changes over time in timing of migratory flights (see Chapter 7 and Lessons 5 and 6). Citizen science data also are useful in tracking the spread of invasive species. For example, the network of birders participating in eBird and FeederWatch documented the rapid advance across North America of the non-native Eurasian Collared-Dove.

Some citizen science projects are local in scope and focus on restoring or preserving vital habitats for selected species. In Syracuse, New York, water-monitoring data collected by high school students led to regulations that protected the stream running through their school yard from potentially being degraded by a proposed new development. Others are local in scope but add to efforts at a national or international scale. In YardMap, for example, citizen scientists use the project website to document habitat improvements they are making in their yards, school yards, or other green spaces, and collectively they become part of a growing conservation community focused on sharing strategies to create more bird habitat across the continent (see Lesson 7). Scientists are interested in using their data to investigate questions such as these:

- What practices improve the wildlife value of residential landscapes?

- Which of these practices have the greatest impact?

- Over how large an area do we have to implement these practices to really make a difference?

Whether or not students contribute data to citizen science projects, they can make productive use of the data available online. With maps produced through Journey North, for example, students track annual migrations of organisms ranging from whales to hummingbirds and track signs of spring such as emergence of earthworms and bursting of buds (see Lessons 4 and 8). Data visualization tools provided through eBird enable students to determine which bird species reside in their hometown year-round and which are migratory (see Lessons 5 and 6).

The 15 lessons in this book portray a rich diversity of ways in which students can both contribute to citizen science and make productive use of its outputs, learning science and math through working with real data and engaging in authentic practices of science as recommended in the *Next Generation Science Standards*. These lessons represent just the tip of the iceberg. We hope they will inspire you to seek out citizen science projects beyond those included here, selecting from the ever-growing assortment of projects spanning from local to global in order to meet your interests and curricular needs.

On the Web

- JellyWatch (*www.jellywatch.org*): A site for recording sightings of jellyfish and other marine organisms

- Lost Ladybug Project (*www.lostladybug.org*): A project dedicated to documenting distribution of North America ladybug species through photos contributed by citizen scientists

- Monarch Larva Monitoring Project (*www.mlmp.org*): A project that aims to understand how and why populations of monarch butterflies vary in time and space, with a focus on the breeding season in North America

- Save Our Streams, Izaak Walton League of America (*www.iwla.org*): A national watershed education and outreach program

References

Cooper, C. 2012a. Researcher's perspective: A citizen science fix for data junkies. PLOS Blogs, CitizenSci. December 12, 2012. *http://blogs.plos.org/citizensci/2012/12/12/ researchers-perspective-a-citizen-science-fix-for-data-junkies*

Cooper, C. 2012b. Stone soup for Thanksgiving: Understanding bird disease through citizen science. Scientific American Guest Blog, November 21, 2012. *http://blogs. scientificamerican.com/guest-blog/2012/11/21/stone-soup-for-thanksgiving- understanding-bird-disease-through-citizen-science*

Dickinson, J. L., J. Shirk, D. Bonter, R. Bonney, R. L. Crain, J. Martin, T. Phillips, and K. Purcell. 2012. The current state of citizen science as a tool for ecological research and public engagement. *Frontiers in Ecology and the Environment* 10 (6): 291–297.

Howard, E., and A. K. Davis. 2009. The fall migration flyways of monarch butterflies in eastern North America revealed by citizen scientists. *Journal of Insect Conservation* 13 (3): 279–286.

Miller, T. 2008. Quoted in terminology and controversy. *The Volunteer Monitor* 19 (1): 2.

Oberhauser, K. S., and M. D. Prysby. 2008. Citizen science: Creating a research army for conservation. *American Entomologist* 54 (2): 97–99.

Chapter 2
Why Use Citizen Science in Your Teaching?

Too often, students think of science as a static collection of facts rather than an ongoing process of discovery in which they can play a part. Unlike the traditional "cookbook" approach to school laboratory assignments, citizen science offers opportunities for students to engage in authentic investigations. Rather than learning from canned data sets, they can view data they have collected within a broader context of data submitted by others. In place of following prescribed protocols to verify known principles, they use protocols to collect and analyze data that feed into projects of importance in their local communities and beyond (Kountoupes and Oberhauser 2008). And instead of memorizing the "Scientific Method," they can engage in inquiry and discover for themselves the multifaceted nature of scientific research. This directly supports the *Next Generation Science Standards* mandate for students not only to "know" science concepts but also to "use their understanding to investigate the natural world through the practices of science inquiry" (Achieve Inc. 2013, Appendix F, p. 1). As explained in *A Framework for K–12 Science Education* on which these standards are based, "Engaging in the practices of science helps students understand how scientific knowledge develops; such direct involvement gives them an appreciation of the wide range of approaches that are used to investigate, model, and explain the world" (NRC 2012, p. 42).

In a variety of ways, citizen science creates opportunities for students to connect with the natural world, gain scientific skills, and learn key science concepts related to topics such as life cycles, habitats, adaptation, and interrelationships between living organisms and the environment (see Appendix 3, p. 203). The lessons and case studies in this book provide a variety of ideas for involving students in investigations using authentic data and online analysis tools. Whether or not your classes go outdoors, these opportunities will connect your students in new ways with the natural world.

Cross-Curricular Connections

Students' natural history observations can be used to tie together various topics across the school year, adding real-world personal connections into topics ranging from cell division to organismal growth to interactions between organisms and the environment. Citizen science projects also can extend far beyond science class. For example, using an approach she calls "transdiciplinary," fifth-grade teacher

Mary Anstey weaves her students' participation in Project BudBurst into lessons in language arts, math, and technology. She says that such experiences make her students "more precise observers of nature" and sparks interest even in those who previously had not been excited about science or the outdoors (Mayer 2010, p. 174).

Students read and interpret nonfiction when they research the natural history of their selected species. They gain experience in expository writing when they describe its seasonal changes, and they employ math skills in making measurements and analyzing their data. And when students submit their data online, they see firsthand the role of technology in collecting, organizing, analyzing, and visualizing scientific data. Geography as well as math skills come into play in comparing their findings with others displayed online. And when students from a school submit data year after year to the same project, they gain the opportunity to view their data within the perspective of trends over time—a foundation of scientific research that is not typically built into student investigations.

Healthier Kids, Healthier Planet

Amid growing concern about the health of children and the environment, today's student often knows more about tropical rain forests in South America and deserts in Africa than the habitats and wildlife in their own neighborhood or community. Participating in citizen science gets children active in observing and appreciating nature. For some, watching birds, insects, or frogs will become a lifelong hobby that takes them outside and keeps them connected with the natural world. Students' appreciation of nature grows when they conduct habitat improvement projects such as planting native species or providing a bird feeder in their school yard. Coupling these efforts with monitoring of birds, butterflies, or other taxonomic groups helps students draw connections between a healthy environment and productive habitats that support diverse forms of life.

Monitoring wildlife can give students new appreciation for what lives nearby and also a new "sense of place" representing a closer connection to their local environment. After listening to frog calls during an amphibian study, for example, one student commented that for the first time he had heard similar frog calls near his home. He was amazed that he had never noticed these sounds before but now was hearing them everywhere. Other students remarked that the fieldwork had helped them overcome fears, learn to love their local reptiles and amphibians, and even develop emotional ties to the habitat itself—describing their research site as "home away from home" and saying that they "loved being in the wild" and "getting in touch with nature."

Over time, this emotional attachment grew into a commitment to the local community. Some continued on their own to volunteer with the citizen science project, and others participated in public events to teach about local species and habitat needs. Many described how they no longer wanted to kill reptiles and instead had begun working to protect them from harm. Many students were thinking about how they could take active roles in protecting their local environment. Who knows where such interest might lead?

Real Scientific Research

Data collection by hundreds of thousands of "boots on the ground" volunteers is opening up whole new forms of research, making it possible to investigate questions that previously had been out of reach. Cornell University ecologist Harry Greene regards such efforts as "absolutely at the core of all biology" and points out that "for most organisms on Earth, we know almost nothing." He describes the volume of data submitted by citizen scientists as "revolutionary" for science as well as for the individuals involved (Fraser 2011).

When the eBird citizen science project celebrated its 100 millionth observation on August 8, 2012, the person who submitted that data point was Liron Gertsman, a 12-year-old from Vancouver, British Columbia. The species with which he hit this milestone was the American Robin, reported on a checklist along with 23 other bird species he had seen that day (Figure 2.1). Cornell Lab of Ornithology Director John Fitzpatrick remarked, "This is a true milestone in the history of field ornithology and citizen science. The power of so much data is only just beginning to be recognized around the world. I look forward to the time when even 100,000,000 observations seems like a quaint number! With eBird taking off so spectacularly now, that day is not so far off, and we are starting to discover some amazing new patterns about the natural world thanks to all these thousands of volunteer observers" (eBird News 2012).

While eBird seeks to build understanding of all bird populations on Earth, most citizen science projects are driven by a more narrowly defined issue or research agenda. For example, the amphibian

FIGURE 2.1.

Liron Gertsman, a 12-year-old who submitted the 100 millionth observation to eBird, surrounded by some of his bird photos

PHOTO OF LIRON BY ANDRE CHAN.

Source: http://ebird.org/content/ebird/news/100000000r

monitoring projects described in Chapter 6 build understanding of the causes for decline in populations of specific species in North and South Carolina. Whether broadly or narrowly focused, citizen science provides a framework within which students can pose their own questions while contributing data toward the overarching goal.

Motivation and Skill Building

When students learn that their data will be entered into a larger database that will be used by scientists to understand important ecological relationships, they take pride in their work and put extra effort into their data collection and analysis. This is a different type of "high stakes" assessment with powerful implications for motivation! In the projects described in this book, students learn a variety of observation skills such as how to track seasonal changes in plant life or identify local frog and toad species by their calls. Knowing that their data will take on a life beyond the classroom motivates students to develop astute observation skills and take extra care in recording data. Discussing the meaning of their findings within the greater context of a citizen science project builds student understanding of how scientific knowledge is generated and revised through a continuous process of discovery in which they are playing a part.

Authentic Student Investigation

Citizen science serves as a framework for authentic student investigations in any setting—urban or rural, with or without access to field or laboratory facilities. Data collection can be as simple as looking out a window and recording what birds come into view or as complex as capturing and tagging turtles for mark and recovery studies. It can take place in a single event or a series of samplings across the seasons or from year to year. Collecting data is only one step in scientific research, and ideally your students' efforts will not end there. Their involvement in citizen science will take on greater meaning if students have the opportunity to analyze and make sense of the data, and where possible to pose their own questions for investigation. The lessons in this book are designed with these goals in mind.

Teachers sometimes worry that student investigations might be too farfetched to lead to productive learning outcomes. Conducting investigations within the context of a citizen science project can allay such worries, letting your classes join in the joy of discovery within the context of a greater community of scientists and educators. Data collection protocols may not leave much room for creativity in sampling, but students can have leeway in posing scientific questions, thinking about variables, and deciding how to analyze the data and interpret their findings within the context of the larger project.

Going beyond collecting and submitting data, citizen science provides opportunities to conduct two key research steps commonly omitted in student research. Before launching into a new line of investigation, professional scientists typically begin by reviewing the literature so that they can learn from and build upon this body of work. As their research progresses, they seek to publish and present their own findings. Because students do not have ready access to scientific journals and conferences, their investigations typically are planned in more of a vacuum and end with a report viewed only by their teacher rather than made available to a broader audience. As a result, students rarely have the chance to base their scientific questions on what has been learned before. And at the conclusion of their investigations, they rarely have the chance to make their results public to inform future investigations and continually refine our collective knowledge about the natural world. Citizen science can fill these gaps by providing online data, tools for visualization and analysis, and annual summaries that portray the current state of knowledge. Students contribute data, and in some cases also have opportunities to share their analyses and reports with a broader community of peers and professionals.

Data Analysis and Interpretation

Citizen science provides opportunities for students to analyze their own data and the data of others, looking for patterns and developing explanations from evidence. When students come up with unexpected results, typically their first response is to assume that they must have done something wrong. However, this may not be the case, and tracking down the source of the discrepant results provides an ideal opportunity for critical thinking and learning about the process of scientific discovery. Not all outlier points are invalid. In the case of butterflies or birds, for example, a species may be seen beyond its usual range due to a hurricane or other unusual weather patterns.

Using online data visualization tools, students can track the signs of spring in local vegetation or the seasonal migrations of whales, hummingbirds, or butterflies. They can determine what species are commonly seen in their area and which ones migrate or remain year-round. Students can view online data to set the scene before doing their own fieldwork, or afterward they can view the data they have collected within the context of broader trends over time or geographic setting. What did other observers report seeing here last year, or this year in an adjacent county?

Liron Gertsman, the 12-year-old birder previously discussed, reflected on this aspect of using the eBird database:

> *Because eBird is an international website, when people submit observations, the migration of bird species is tracked, therefore teaching us more about certain bird species and their migration. eBird also allows people to see the decline and increase in bird populations across the world on amazing charts and graphs, or surprising news about bird species around the world. Every time I come back from birding outings, I go online to eBird, and submit what I saw that day. Then I might look at what other people have recently seen nearby. I really find it incredible that one site can have users from around the world sharing what they see and looking at what other people see. I often rely on eBird to set my destinations for bird watching and that's a big impact that eBird has on my birding life.* (eBird News 2012).

Collecting and submitting data is not essential to productive use of citizen science in your teaching. Without conducting any fieldwork, you still can make productive use of online data and visualization tools to develop students' skills in graphing, data analysis, and interpretation while exploring questions related to concepts such as life cycles, food webs, habitats, behavior, and adaptation.

Identity as a Scientist

Not only can students enjoy developing closer connections with wildlife and habitats through citizen science, they also can build new relationships with each other, with professionals, and with other citizen scientists. Participating in this type of community can overcome the stereotype of scientists in white lab coats working in sterile laboratories. Through citizen science fieldwork, students experience a bit of what it means to be an entomologist, herpetologist, ornithologist, or botanist, implementing authentic research protocols and considering their findings within the context of real-world questions. Through such experiences, students are not just learning science but actually being scientists, contributing findings that collectively build to a broader study. Citizen science may also provide ways to connect students with local experts who are interested in helping with field projects or coming into your classroom to share their knowledge and interest in science. Such interactions help students to identify with a culture of people who appreciate and respect local habitats, plants, and wildlife.

Through citizen science, students also can become local experts in the field they have studied, and learning to think and talk about their investigations builds their identity as scientists. For example, students in the herpetology project described in Chapter 6 shared their new expertise at local and state-level meetings and were proud to be recognized for their ability to identify, handle, and describe local species and habitats. Whether students contribute their own data or make use of online data submitted by others, citizen science offers opportunities to work with real data, participate in a community with professional scientists, and make authentic discoveries. What better way to make school science relevant, enticing, and even fun?

References

Achieve Inc. 2013. *Next Generation Science Standards*. *www.nextgenscience.org/next-generation-science-standards*

Cornell Lab of Ornithology. 2012. *eBird News* (August 13). *http://ebird.org/content/ebird/news/100000000r*

Fraser, C. 2011. Tapping social media's potential to muster a vast green army. *Yale Environment 360* July 11. *http://e360.yale.edu/feature/tapping_social_medias_potential_to_muster_a_vast_green_army/2424*

Kountoupes, D., and K. S. Oberhauser. 2008. Citizen science and youth audiences: Educational outcomes of the Monarch Larva Monitoring Project. *Journal of Community Engagement and Scholarship* 1 (1): 10–20.

Mayer, A. 2010. Phenology and citizen science. *BioScience* 60 (3): 172–175.

National Governors Association Center for Best Practices and Council of Chief State School Officers (NGAC and CCSSO). 2010. *Common core state standards*. Washington, DC: NGAC and CCSSO.

National Research Council (NRC). 2012. *A framework for K–12 science education: Practices, crosscutting concepts, and core ideas*. Washington, DC: National Academies Press.

Chapter 3
Implementation Strategies

Citizen science can fit into your teaching in a variety of ways. This book is meant to provide a jumping off point, and the lessons we've selected are just the beginning. They represent a broad range of topics, taxonomic groups, science process skills, and teaching strategies, and they can be adapted or extended in various ways to meet your interests and needs.

Each lesson is organized around the BSCS 5E Instructional Model to lead students through this progression of steps (Bybee 2009):

1. **Engagement:** Short activities designed to stimulate curiosity and prior knowledge about the topic.

2. **Exploration:** Experiences in which students explore the concept further, possibly through a hands-on activity.

3. **Explanation:** Activities through which students demonstrate their conceptual understanding, process skills, or behaviors, or through which teachers provide explanation to guide students toward deeper understanding.

4. **Elaboration:** Further activities to challenge and extend students' conceptual understanding and skills.

5. **Evaluation:** Opportunities for student and teacher to assess student progress toward achieving the desired learning outcomes.

A Framework for K–12 Science Education (NRC 2012) and the *Next Generation Science Standards* (Achieve Inc. 2013) present the vision that students will be actively engaged in scientific practices related to disciplinary core ideas, and they will learn about science by integrating content knowledge with experience in the practices of scientific inquiry. Students will be engaged with fundamental questions about the natural world and the processes through which scientists investigate and seek answers to these questions. Teachers are being called to cultivate student's scientific habits of mind, develop their capability to engage in scientific investigations, and teach them how to reason in a scientific context. The goal is to nurture students' appreciation for the wide range of approaches used to investigate, model, and explain the world. The *Framework* identifies eight practices for the K–12 science classroom, which are mapped to our lessons in Appendix 1 (see p. 199):

1. Asking questions and defining problems.

2. Developing and using models.

3. Planning and carrying out investigations.

4. Analyzing and interpreting data.

5. Using mathematics and computational thinking.

6. Constructing explanations and designing solutions.

7. Engaging in argument from evidence.

8. Obtaining, evaluating, and communicating information (NRC 2012, p. 42).

The *Framework* also identifies seven crosscutting concepts, which are mapped to our lessons in Appendix 2 (see p. 201):

1. Patterns. Noticing repeating events, describing relationships, classifying objects based on careful observations, and organizing data in ways that makes pattern recognition more apparent.

2. Cause and effect: Mechanism and explanation. Explaining causal relationships using evidence.

3. Scale, proportion, and quantity. Recognizing that the way things work may change with scale, thinking in terms of magnitude.

4. Systems and system models. Acknowledging boundaries, components, resources and flow within and across systems; interdependence within systems; models of systems including the assumptions and limitations associated with the model.

5. Energy and matter: Flows, cycles, and conservation. Explaining how energy and matter transfer in and out of a system.

6. Structure and function. Exploring the relationship between structure and function at many different levels.

7. Stability and change. Understanding how change occurs in nature (NRC 2012, p. 84).

Appendix 3 (p. 203) maps the lessons to specific science topics such as life cycle, adaptation, and habitat, Appendix 4 (p. 205) maps them to science process skills ranging from collaborating to using and understanding maps, and Appendix 5 (p. 207) maps them to primary location and season.

Some of the lessons might provide ideas that you would like to adapt, for example to focus on a different taxonomic group. Others are written around regional citizen science databases that are not applicable in your part of the country, but perhaps a similar project exists in your area that will meet your needs. The Citizen Science Central and SciStarter websites aggregate information about the ever-growing assortment of projects and provide ways to discover which are best aligned with your goals.

Connections to Common Core State Standards

Citizen science has the potential to support various aspects of the *Common Core State Standards* in English language arts and mathematics, which are being implemented in many states. The Language Arts standards specify that students should be able to "delineate and evaluate the argument and specific claims in a text, including the validity of the reasoning as well as the relevance and sufficiency of the evidence" (NGAC and CCSSO 2010, p. 35). Many of the lessons in this book call for students to read background information to learn the context for their investigations. As they practice making inferences from this reading and from their own scientific data, they are practicing the skills of scientific argumentation and evaluation of reasoning. In summarizing their findings and using evidence to support their explanations, they are building key literacy skills.

In accord with the *Common Core State Standards* in mathematics, many of the lessons in this book engage students in the following mathematical practices (NGAC and CCSSO 2010, pp. 6–7):

- Making sense of problems and persevering in solving them.

- Reasoning abstractly and quantitatively.

- Constructing viable arguments and critiquing the reasoning of others.

- Using appropriate tools strategically.

- Attending to precision.

In middle school, students should use concepts of ratio and rate to solve problems, and they should begin using statistical thinking, for example, to draw inferences about populations based on samples. These calculations and inferences come to life when students use real citizen science data addressing issues of relevance in their communities and beyond.

Potential Hurdles

Given all the challenges faced in today's classrooms, it may be tempting to think that citizen science doesn't provide a good fit. We hope that the responses below will overcome any hurdles you may be facing in thinking about involving your classes in opportunities afforded by citizen science.

No Time to Add Anything New Into Your Curriculum?

The lessons presented here were selected to help teach required concepts and skills in powerful new ways rather than adding yet another item into your overpacked curriculum. Using the tables in Appendixes 1 through 5, you can find lessons that meet specific curricular mandates by engaging students in genuine scientific research.

No Access to a Natural Area, or No Time to Get Outside?

Even if collecting their own field data is not an option, students can pose questions for inquiry using online data collected by others, on topics ranging from whale communications (Lesson 1) to butterfly migration (Lesson 2).

No Access to Computers?

Most of the lessons do not require access to a computer lab. With a single computer and projector or interactive whiteboard, you can project citizen science web resources and work collectively as a class to pose questions, view relevant data outputs, plan investigations, and submit data collected by your students. Even with no classroom access to the internet, it still is possible to engage students in data exploration and analysis using citizen science data outputs that have been downloaded in advance. Increasingly, even cell phones can be used to upload or view citizen science data, which can come in handy in field settings or in a classroom without internet access.

Doubts About Student Research?

Giving students the opportunity to design and conduct their own investigations can be daunting because of your need to ensure positive learning outcomes. Citizen science provides a framework within which students can readily pose scientific questions that are relevant and realistic. Following provided protocols ensures that their data collection methods make sense without constraining their ability to conduct investigations of their own design. And citizen science provides opportunities rarely open to students to analyze and interpret their data within the context of broader findings and trends.

Using Online Data and Visualization Tools

No matter whether your students will be conducting fieldwork outdoors or staying inside for investigations within your classroom, they can pose scientific questions, analyze authentic data, and engage in the processes of scientific research.

- Before conducting their own observations, students can view online data to get started on thinking about the selected organisms and perhaps to generate questions before they begin collecting data of their own. For example, in Lesson 12 students view citizen science data to determine what frog species live in their region before learning the calls of these species and then heading out into the field to conduct their own survey of calling amphibians.

- After collecting data, students can put their findings into a broader context by viewing the larger citizen science data set over time and/or geographic setting. They might choose to view trends in sightings of a specific species over a period of several years, or to determine the geographic range of a species that is seen in their town only rarely. For example, in Lesson 3 students inventory terrestrial invertebrates in a selected study plot then go online to the Hands on the Land website, where they can submit their data and also pose questions to address using data submitted for that location by classes in previous years or data submitted by others at various sites around the country.

- Without collecting their own field data, students can use online data to investigate questions that you pose or that they select on their own. For example, you might ask students to use eBird data exploration tools to determine what bird species are found in your county and which migrate versus staying year-round. As an extension, they could pose individual questions related to individual species or comparisons between several species of interest (Lesson 6).

Finding the Right Fit

Citizen science offers a world of opportunities for students, but not all citizen science endeavors will provide the right fit with your teaching goals. The first step in assuring a good fit is to select one or more lessons that coincide with the time of year and type of habitat you have in mind. Some lessons can be conducted entirely indoors or in your school yard, whereas others require access to pond or wetland habitats. Appendix 5 (see p. 207) maps the lessons to the season and type of location in which they can best be conducted.

Another consideration is whether you would like your students to participate in all aspects of research or perhaps just pieces of the process. A common criticism of citizen science is that students will not experience the full scientific inquiry process if they merely follow provided data collection protocols and submit their data for analysis and interpretation by professionals. Another possible discrepancy occurs when the questions being posed by professional scientists are too complex to be appropriate for students (Zoellick, Nelson, and Schauffler 2012). The lessons in this book circumvent these issues by engaging students in data analysis and interpretation. In some cases this occurs with data they have collected themselves, and in other cases students use data displayed online.

Keep in mind that citizen science plays dual roles, engaging volunteers in data collection and analysis while also enabling professional scientists to conduct research that would not be possible without this type of assistance. Successful integration of citizen science into your teaching requires selecting a project in which the role for volunteers meshes well with your teaching goals. The lessons presented here portray a wide range of projects and ways in which they can productively be integrated into student engagement in science. We hope they will help you to envision exciting ways in which you can weave citizen science into your teaching to bring content and practices to life for your students.

On the Web

- Citizen Science Central (*www.birds.cornell.edu/citscitoolkit*): A portal for searching citizen science projects by topic and/or location

- Common Core State Standards Initiative (*www.corestandards.org*): The source for Common Core documents

- SciStarter (*www.scistarter.com*): A portal for searching citizen science projects by topic and/or location

References

Achieve Inc. 2013. *Next Generation Science Standards. www.nextgenscience.org/next-generation-science-standards*

Bybee, R. W. 2009. *The BSCS 5E instructional model and 21st century skills*. Paper commissioned by The National Academies, Board on Science Education. *www7. nationalacademies.org/bose/1Bybee_21st%20Century_Paper.pdf*

National Governors Association Center for Best Practices and Council of Chief State School Officers (NGAC and CCSSO). 2010. *Common core state standards*. Washington, DC: NGAC and CCSSO.

National Research Council (NRC). 2012. *A framework for K–12 science education: Practices, crosscutting concepts, and core ideas.* Washington, DC: National Academies Press.

Zoellick, B., S. J. Nelson, and M. Schauffler. 2012. Participatory science and education: Bringing both views into focus. *Frontiers in Ecology and the Environment* 10 (6): 310–313.

Additional Resources

Ryken, A. E., P. Otto, K. Pritchard, and K. Owens. 2007. *Field investigations: Using outdoor environments to foster student learning of scientific processes.* Pacific Education Institute, Olympia, WA. *www.pacificeducationinstitute.org/workspace/resources/field-investigation-guide-updated-april-2009.pdf*
Summary: Provides guidance in preparing students to conduct outdoor investigations, building field investigations from student questions, and using data collected over time to identify patterns and relationships.

Schaus, J. M., R. Bonney, A. J. Rosenberg, and C. B. Phillips. 2007. *BirdSleuth: Investigating evidence.* Ithaca, NY: Cornell Lab of Ornithology. *www.birds.cornell.edu/birdsleuth/inquiry-resources/investigating-evidence-1/investigating-evidence*
Summary: Guides each step of student investigations focusing on birds, from initial observations through posing questions, conducting research, and analyzing and presenting the results.

Chapter 4
Case Study: Connecting With Students Through Birds

by Jennifer Fee, Liam Curley, and Nancy M. Trautmann

During their bus ride to school through urban Yonkers, New York, students in Margaret Scaglione's class watched the sky for birds. Coming from rough neighborhoods, some were not allowed to spend free time outside. But with faces pressed to the bus windows, they rode within two blocks of the Hudson River and noticed songbirds and hawks in flight. In the classroom, they excitedly reported these observations. "It was a suspension of disbelief for me," Margaret says, "to realize that it really mattered to them—that they had become aware of these birds because they had begun really looking."

Doing bird-related citizen science doesn't require a deep knowledge of birds or a wealth of resources. Margaret's class made bird feeders out of recycled soda bottles and hung them within view of the classroom windows. "What I was interested in, and what the kids came away with, was a sense of belonging in a world of creatures," she says. "For these students that's a large understanding." On a class field trip Margaret's students were walking in the Bronx Botanical Garden when several started pointing in the air. As classes from other schools passed by, her students pointed out a colorful Baltimore Oriole, began explaining its field marks and remarked that orioles might come to your feeder if you put out oranges— "something I don't remember telling them," Margaret laughs.

Norma Griffin, a fourth-grade teacher in a small rural New York town, assigns local bird species to her students. Each student learns what his or her species looks and sounds like, what it eats, what type of habitat it prefers, and what kind of nest it builds. Her students go into the school yard to collect materials they think their bird might eat or use for nest building. Each student becomes an expert on a single species and uses this knowledge to support the rest of the class as they observe and count birds.

As students learn to identify birds by sight and sound, they can join with other citizen scientists in contributing observations to a variety of bird-focused projects including eBird and Project FeederWatch. Any class can participate, whether urban, suburban, or rural. In fact, eBird accepts data about any bird, seen at anytime, anywhere in the world. With over three million observations submitted each month, it incorporates observations from every continent and represents most of the world's approximately 10,000 bird species. Project FeederWatch focuses on periodic counts of birds viewed at feeders in North America, so students can contribute data without leaving their classroom.

The data submitted by students and other citizen science participants help researchers to better understand bird distribution, abundance, and habitat requirements—crucial information in determining population trends and conservation needs. It is motivational for students to know that their data will be put to use addressing real-world issues of local and global concern: "It gives them the ability to genuinely participate in science, to know that their observations count for something and will be used," says Phil Kahler, a middle school teacher in Oregon, "but it also requires the student to somehow be careful. It motivates the kids to get out there and make science. When students realize that this is important data that someone will be using to make connections they otherwise couldn't make, they're motivated to realize 'I'm helping.'" As a seventh-grade student put it, "Scientists can't be everywhere, so kids from all over can record data and send it in."

Learning With Citizen Science Data

Either before or after observing local birds, classes can use online data exploration tools to determine what birds have been sighted in their community, find trends, and discuss various interpretations of the data (Figure 4.1).

Minneapolis seventh-grade teacher Katie Humason takes her students to a local nature center every fall where they build bird feeders from kits. The students decide which birds they would like to attract, and then determine what type of feeder to build and what kind of food to provide. They create a feeding station including about a dozen feeders on the front lawn of school. Although they can't see the feeders from their classroom, they go outside each week to count birds and submit their counts to eBird. Later, they explore eBird data online to address questions such as, "Are we seeing the same birds here as they do in Florida?" or "How does temperature affect our bird counts?"

If a school submits citizen science data over multiple years, students can view their own data within the context of site-specific trends. When Phil Kahler's classes began observing birds in 1996, for example, dark-eyed juncos were the most abundant species at their school's feeding station. Three years later, students noticed a dramatic decline in dark-eyed juncos along with a huge influx of house sparrows, a species not previously recorded in that location. Wondering what might be causing these changes, they speculated that it could be coincidental, or maybe juncos had been driven off by nearby residential development, or perhaps by the sparrow invasion. One student investigated whether eBird data showed similar junco declines elsewhere in Oregon. Seeing no widespread downward trend during this time period, she concluded that habitat loss in their area was the likely cause. Her

FIGURE 4.1.

eBird, like many citizen science projects, offers online tools for data exploration and analysis.

study was published in Classroom BirdScope (renamed BirdSleuth Investigator in 2012), a student journal published annually by the Cornell Lab of Ornithology.

Teaching sixth graders in Connecticut, Sanjiv Maliakal is impressed with the way that bird watching affects students who don't excel in more traditional classroom activities. He's found that these students take well to being outside and using their senses to observe and listen to birds. He has noticed that students who are not adept at memorizing vocabulary may excel at identifying birds: "It's nice to see the confidence build when you go beyond the 'terminology' of science." He hears stories about how kids went to the park with their folks and saw "such and such" a bird. The fact that on a Monday, kids come back and say "We were sledding and we saw 'this, this, and this' shows the connection they have developed to birds." These young people are cluing into their surroundings and their environment a lot more, gaining appreciation for just being outside. Sanjiv adds, "I think that is so crucial nowadays when kids are spending more and more time indoors and being wowed by technology. It's cool to hear that kids are still making that connection with nature."

In addition to participating in eBird, Sanjiv's sixth graders also do an independent experiment using inexpensive feeders that he lends out. About half of the kids opt to do their projects at home. He reports that families say how much they've enjoyed having bird watching become a part of their family routine, and how impressed they've been with their children's excitement about these activities. "We had grandparents' day at the schools—the grandparents are really into it too." As Sanjiv says, "it's nice for the kids to have that experience, and to share that experience with their grandparents."

From Data to Modeling

Students typically learn about models as a way to describe and visualize molecules, and sometimes they use simple models to change variables and see responses in a system. They may not realize that models also provide powerful research tools for scientists. The natural history databases being built through citizen science are enabling scientists to build complex data-rich models that are useful for both research and education.

Using a model that combines eBird data with information on habitat, climate, human population, and demographics, scientists have begun creating animated maps that vividly illustrate migration and habitat preferences of selected species. For example, the chimney swift map "lights up" in the summer in urban areas where their preferred nesting sites are plentiful, whereas the forest-dwelling indigo bunting shows an entirely different spatial pattern (Figure 4.2).

FIGURE 4.2.

Summer abundance of chimney swifts (left) and indigo buntings (right) indicate opposite influence of human population density on nesting habitat for these two bird species.

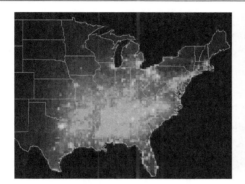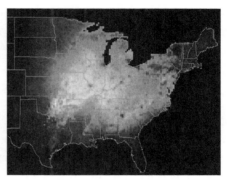

The models predict movement throughout the year and make it possible for scientists to explore various scenarios such as how migration timing might change with alteration of landscape or climate.

For students, the maps offer compelling visualization of the interconnectedness of species and their habitats—and a new way of seeing the importance of both local and distant habitats in supporting healthy bird populations. See Lesson 5, "Animated Maps for Animated Discussions," for further ideas about classroom activities featuring these maps created through modeling using eBird citizen science data.

Inquiry and Citizen Science

Students can go beyond bird counts and use their observations to ask open-ended questions, conduct original investigations, and engage in new ways with the natural world. Norma, the fourth-grade teacher in New York, says that she uses this aspect of the curriculum to help her students realize that "we are all scientists" who can keep coming up with questions. "'Why are these birds eating gravel?' a student will ask me, and I'll say 'Hmmm … I don't know. How would we find something like that out?'" These investigations take the form of creative experiments, observational studies, primary source research, and querying the citizen science databases.

Norma and others base their teaching about birds on a curriculum called BirdSleuth, designed by the Cornell Lab of Ornithology to involve middle school students in citizen science projects and inquiry investigations. Students begin by learning how to identify a few local birds and progress into making observations, asking questions, and then conducting investigations. They can use the eBird database to find out about their local birds either before or after conducting their own observations, and they can contribute their bird observation data to the ever-growing database generated by bird watchers throughout the world.

At the heart of BirdSleuth is a set of free downloadable lessons, called Investigating Evidence, designed to help teachers guide students through independent investigations focusing on birds (Schaus, Bonney, Rosenberg, and Phillips 2007). Whether using their own bird observations or looking for patterns in online data collected by others, BirdSleuth encourages students to develop their own research questions and then design and conduct an investigation addressing a question of their choice. Students have done everything from playing recordings of animals sounds (such as birds of prey or lions) near feeders, to dressing up as trees and bears to see how close they can get to a flock of birds. The Cornell Lab of Ornithology publishes the most innovative of these student scientific reports each year in its BirdSleuth Investigator publication. Norma says that the potential for their work to become published excites her students. "It's a way of taking control of their own learning process. It's about nurturing curiosity and initiative and that's what it's all about: creating lifelong learners."

Viewing citizen science outputs provides opportunities for students to observe patterns and trends, develop inferences, and discuss various interpretations of the data. "It inspires the kids to see what's been done before," Phil says, "but also to come up with questions nobody else has asked." Students can even conduct investigations exclusively using online data. Pat Killian's middle school class in Corning, New York, for example, has learned that they can explore their environment without leaving the classroom. "They can explore online data and pose questions ranging from migration patterns to what kinds of birds live where, and they can use these questions to plan their own experiments or studies." This is part of being a 21st-century learner, Pat says, being able to integrate knowledge that's already there, and to be web and technology savvy. "The world is shrinking," she says, "and the kids understand that more than we do." For them it is as easy as, "Well, we'll just find someone in Russia who knows. This may seem far-fetched. But more and more, this connection is becoming our reality."

Each year, the students in Taylor Abbott's ninth-grade biology classes at North Davis Preparatory Academy in Utah track migrations of selected bird species using eBird maps. They investigate the reasons for these flights, the types of habitats needed to support selected species, and the adaptations required for survival in these habitats. To sharpen their mathematical skills, Taylor's students analyze potential uses of the various types of graphs that eBird produces. And finally, they discuss the importance of tracking population trends and how "everyday civilians" can contribute to this key facet of science.

Going Beyond

BirdSleuth teachers have begun using citizen science and inquiry as a jumping-off point for online wiki-based collaboration among classes. Students in Oregon and Florida, for example, connect in a meaningful way as they read each other's research questions and reports and provide peer review. "It's a level of professionalism that students don't usually have," says Phil Kahler, the collaborating teacher in Oregon, "and it bonds the scientific community that the students get to be in." While the students appreciate the social aspect, the teachers report that the students take their work more seriously, knowing that an "outsider" will be evaluating their work.

After exchanging peer reviews, the students Skyped with each other, meeting their peer review partners "face to face." Students got curious and began asking questions such as, "Are our friends in Florida seeing the same birds as we are?" They compared data using the eBird database and learned that while there was some overlap, there also were some surprising differences: Each locale had a jay, a crow, and a goldfinch, but the actual species were different! This experience led to discussions and new understandings of speciation, evolution, and adaptation. Elizabeth Eubanks, the collaborating teacher in Florida, reflected,

> This has provided me with a new way to teach ecosystems and habitat through inquiry and also use the Cornell Lab's innovative maps, graphs, and charts and citizen science data. Collecting and using real-world data is highly motivating for students and allows me to teach science content in a way that feels relevant to their lives. I believe that educational networking has great potential for helping students to comprehend the scientific method while they edit and assist other students with their lab reports. And this "paperless" project is great for the environment… enhancing technology skills will benefit not only students but our planet, as well.

From Inquiry Into Action

Once students start monitoring local birds or conducting investigations with online citizen science data, many become inspired to undertake habitat improvement or other conservation projects. For example, Frederick Atwood at Flint Hill School in Virginia engages his students in inquiry-based learning using eBird data because "kids can see the success of conservation and apply it to helping to protect their local bird populations." His students conduct conservation projects such as building nest boxes for eastern bluebirds or wood ducks. Both of these species are cavity nesters whose breeding success tends to be limited by competition for available cavities. Bluebird populations fell in the early 20th century as introduced aggressive species such as European starlings and house sparrows took over available nest holes. Beginning in the 1960s, nest box campaigns alleviated much of this competition, and bluebird numbers have been recovering. When Frederick's students create eBird graphs showing rise in native bluebird populations with decline in numbers of invasive sparrows, they see the importance of checking their bluebird boxes weekly to remove sparrow nests. Frederick notes, "Kids can see the success of conservation and can even apply it to helping to protect their local bird populations."

In State College, Pennsylvania, Howard Pillot's students have entered their sightings into eBird over the past six years. Howard says "Citizen science makes us all more aware of our environment—both the good and the bad parts." He's seen that this awareness can create personal interest and responsibility by "getting youth to ask really good questions about how we're treating the Earth and whether we're being good stewards."

On the Web

- eBird (*http://eBird.org*): A citizen science project that collects and displays data about birds from around the world

- Project FeederWatch (*www.FeederWatch.org*): A citizen science project that collects data about feeder birds in the United States and Canada

- BirdSleuth Investigator (*www.birdsleuth.org/student-publication*): The Cornell Lab of Ornithology's student research publication

Additional Resources

Fee, J., and N. M. Trautmann. 2012. Connecting to your community through birds and citizen science. *Science Scope* 36 (3): 62–68.
Summary: Discusses use of bird-related citizen science in middle school science

Schaus, J. M., R. Bonney, A. J. Rosenberg, and C. B. Phillips. 2007. *BirdSleuth: Investigating evidence.* Ithaca, NY: Cornell Lab of Ornithology. *www.birds.cornell.edu/birdsleuth/investigating-evidence*
Summary: Free lessons that guide each step of student investigations, from initial observations through posing questions, conducting research, and analyzing and presenting the results

Trautmann, N. M., J. Fee, and P. Kahler. 2012. Flying into inquiry. *The Science Teacher* 79 (9): 45–50.
Summary: Provides ideas for use of bird-related citizen science in high school biology classes

Chapter 5
Case Study:
The Mysteries of Monarchs

by NancyLee R. Bergey

I think the most meaningful science [experience] was when you came to [a Philadelphia public school] to release the monarch butterflies. I have to admit, I am not the biggest fan of insects, but it was nice to see my students really excited to learn. I watched some of the kids go from whining about how they didn't want to stay outside anymore to joyfully participating in the activity ... It [served] as another reminder of how kids are naturally curious about the world around them. As a teacher I need to find ways to keep my students active learners, and experiments are a nice and easy way to do that. As I walked upstairs with the class, they were surprisingly quiet.... I believe that they were quiet because of the science experiment. They were able to let out their energy so that they could focus in class.

—Charmaine Giles, student teacher

Citizen science related to monarch butterflies offers many points of entry, and you can decide whether to jump in with both feet or just dangle a toe. Students can raise, tag, and release butterflies through Monarch Watch. They can observe the arrival of the first monarchs in your area and submit the date to Journey North. Or they can conduct meaningful math analyses using nearly two decades of data collected at Cape May, New Jersey, though the Monarch Monitoring Project.

Cross-curricular connections are myriad as well. Beyond the obvious connections to science and math, monarch study can be the basis for geography studies as students follow yearly migration, or economics and ethics lessons as they consider trade-offs between logging versus conservation in the region of Mexico where monarchs gather each winter. Susannah Gund used monarchs as the basis for an integrated unit that she wrote and taught in her student teaching year in a sixth-grade classroom in a Philadelphia public school that was pressed to achieve adequate progress to meet federal mandates. Susannah says, "As I started to think more and more about whether I could meet some of the sixth-grade standards through monarchs, I became captivated by how we know what we know about monarchs, and I realized that this unit could be as much about asking questions as anything else—a concept, in my mind, perfect for sixth graders."

The Power of Many

Susannah started her unit with data from Journey North, a project in which students share information about seasonal phenomena such as emergence of tulip blooms and first sightings of monarch butterflies, whooping cranes, and several humming-bird species during their spring migrations. In watching such events unfold over time across the continent, students see how individual data points become more meaningful when aggregated and compared with data from other locations.

In Susannah's class, students checked the website each Thursday for updates on where monarchs had been spotted that week, and they practiced using latitude and longitude coordinates while adding the new data to a map in their classroom. Soon the students were making predictions, which could be checked the follow-ing week. This process of making and testing predictions is an important aspect of scientific research, and Susannah shared her students' excitement in following real data to address real questions for which the answer is not known in advance.

The Journey North website displays new weekly data through a series of maps, using color to differentiate between weeks. Animated maps accelerate these changes, and students have remarked that this is like watching the monarchs migrate. The Journey North site also includes emergence dates for milkweed, the obligatory food of monarch caterpillars, providing an opportunity for students to consider the importance of timing of migration with availability of food resources. Journey North goes beyond just numbers, too. As new data are added each week, Journey North staff post comments and engaging questions, sometimes connecting with relevant current items in the news. For example, on May 21, 2011, they posted:

> *The migration continued to advance during the past week—slowly, steadily, and a little early. We're still waiting for the big surge in numbers to occur. Is the drought in Texas affecting timing this spring? Did drought drive the monarchs out of Texas early? Explore how data citizen scientists are collecting helps answer key questions like these.*

A one-page article described the drought and included photos, a map, pie chart, and bar graph. Analyzing these materials provides opportunities for practicing key science literacy skills.

Students at another Philadelphia school participated in Journey North's "Symbolic Migration" by creating beautiful paper monarchs to be sent to schools in Mexico. The students decorated their butterflies with simple messages to the Mexican students, such as "Thanks for taking care of the butterflies." Two bilingual students used their language skill as classmates crowded around and asked them to translate their intended phrases into Spanish. In the spring the class was excited to receive a package from Mexico. The paper monarchs that had come back were not the same ones they had sent. According to the teacher, "this is much more realistic. We did not get back as many as we sent. Not all of the monarchs live to make the journey North. And we did not get the same ones, which of course is reasonable. We would not expect to be able to find the same butterfly we released, back in our own schoolyard." Instead, the students were able to read the messages sent by other U.S. students, and in some cases responses written by Mexican students.

Monitoring Marked Monarchs

Monarchs can be raised in the classroom, then tagged and released. Using tiny stickers applied and later read by citizen scientists, Monarch Watch makes it possible to track individual organisms across space and time. Raising, tagging, and releasing monarchs inspires students to learn about the hurdles these organisms face and to care about their survival.

FIGURE 5.1.

A monarch bearing a tag produced by the Monarch Watch project

The Monarch Watch team at the University of Kansas has been monitoring monarch migration for 20 years. Each participant purchases stickers portraying a phone number, e-mail address, and unique alphanumeric identifier (Figure 5.1, p. 35).

The citizen scientist attaches the sticker to the lower wing of a monarch and records on a data sheet the date and location, whether the monarch was caught in the wild or raised in captivity, and its sex. (Don't know how to tell a male from a female monarch? Ask any student who has participated in this project. That is something they never forget!). The data sheet is sent to Monarch Watch so that tagged butterflies caught or found later in life can be traced back to the location and timing of their release. Whether or not students raise and tag their own monarchs, they can analyze monarch migrations using Monarch Watch data (see Lesson 2, "It's Been a Hard Day's Flight: Determining Daily Flight Distances of Monarch Butterflies").

Of course many monarchs die in the overwintering grounds in Mexico. One effort by Monarch Watch has been to pay local Mexican citizens to collect fallen monarchs that have tags. This makes the monarchs a source of income for the residents and may help preserve the land from logging. Students in in many U.S. schools raise money to support this effort in consideration of the complex issue of wanting to preserve critical habitat while recognizing the needs of the local people.

Improving Habitat

The reliance of monarchs on milkweed availability suggests the question, "Could we raise some?" The answer is unequivocally "Yes!" You can raise milkweed of a whole variety of species. Providing nectar for migrating butterflies is another way to help ameliorate the fragmentation of habitat that endangers monarch migration. You can create a butterfly garden that is both beautiful and educational for your class and the larger community. These days there are myriad sources for ideas about butterfly gardens on the web, but Monarch Watch can help you get started, and you can even register your site as an official Monarch Waystation once it is established (*www.monarchwatch.org/waystations*). Developing a plan for the site, deciding which plants to include (and why), and figuring out how to fund the work would make an outstanding service-learning project for students. You could even map your site and record habitat improvements using the YardMap citizen science website (see Lesson 7, "Habitat Matters: YardMap Your School Yard!").

Deep Understanding

When student teacher Susannah Gund purchased larvae from Monarch Watch, her plans reached far beyond the simple observation of metamorphosis that might be expected in a sixth-grade classroom. Susannah's class delved into questions such as:

- How can we "trust" data? What steps can we take to make our data/data collection more reliable?

- How can we most effectively share our data and analyze the data collected by others?

- What are the different ways that we can record our Monarch data? Is one way more valuable than another?

- What kinds of questions can we ask about metamorphosis?

The students engaged in real science, with expectations that they would clearly organize data, make predictions, and explain connections between data and inferences. They found the mean, mode, and range in each series of numbers, created graphs, and generated questions based on their observations (see Lesson 2).

Use of statistics is unusual in sixth grade but made sense to Susannah's students in the context of wanting an overall picture of how their milkweed plants and caterpillars were growing, rather than concentrating on the growth of just one individual. Studying real organisms elicited meaningful discussions about what to measure and how to report it. Students noticed, for example, that rapid growth of their caterpillars was not adequately captured by measurements of length or even width. This led to an investigation of the comparison between linear measure and volume, and they found that a single millimeter of growth in each direction (from 5 × 1 mm to 6 × 2 mm) yields more than a four-fold increase in volume.

This led into discussion about appropriate approximations in science. How do you find the volume of a caterpillar? You can estimate with the formula for the volume of a cylinder (pi × radius² × height), but for our purposes would the volume of a square prism (length × width × width) serve just as well? Such approximations are common in science but rarely explored in K–12 classrooms.

Doing It by the Numbers

Another aspect of being a citizen scientist is using data collected by others. At Cape May, New Jersey, the Monarch Monitoring Project has been keeping weekly monarch census data during September and October when large numbers of butterflies are most likely to collect and wait for the right conditions to cross the Delaware Bay. The project uses a monitoring protocol to ensure data consistency, providing an opportunity to talk with students about the importance of standardized methods in collecting consistent data over time or across sites.

The data assembled on the Monarch Monitoring Project website make possible a variety of analyses. You could pose a simple question such as, "How many more monarchs were seen on the first week of October than in the first week of September in 2000?" More complex analyses could include creating graphs, looking for trends, and trying to determine potential causes. The most open-ended and potentially exciting option would be to show students the data and ask what questions come to their minds. For example, a large difference between the numbers in the same week between one year and another might raise questions about the weather. With the internet, students could readily investigate weather conditions during those intervals. But perhaps the issue is longer term. What were the conditions in the overwintering grounds during each of the previous winters, and how might these conditions have affected butterfly populations the following fall? The idea that the data can both raise questions and help answer them is powerful, and students see this activity as quite different from the usual math class exercise. See Lesson 2 for another approach to using interest in monarchs to spur deep discussion of data analysis.

The Social Nature of Science

Many students have a stereotypical vision of science and scientists—either the frizzly-haired white male in a lab coat working with chemicals in his lab, or the Marie Curie image of a woman working alone in an unheated shed, oblivious to the hardship because she is so engrossed in her work. Neither is an accurate image of how science is done today, nor an image that will draw students into science. In reality, scientific teams work together in and out of the lab, and meaningful collaborations happen between researchers working half a world apart. Increasingly, scientists from different fields are learning that cross-disciplinary studies yield the most interesting and meaningful results. Susannah sees the potential for monarch work in helping to overcome students' incorrect and unappealing views about science:

The emphasis on citizen science encourages students to see the study of science and the natural world as a deeply social and interconnected process, emphasizing the social nature of all sciences. The use (and abuse) of natural resources and the consideration of preservation and the economy are also elements of the social studies standards for sixth grade, which will certainly be highlighted through considerations of the monarchs' winter habitat and conflict over resource preservation in Mexico.

And just as there are multiple ways to start investigating monarchs, there are myriad ways to expand the study. Quoting Susannah again:

[T]hrough the focus on questioning, citizen science, and how we know what we know, the possibilities for this topic are almost endless. Students might take their questions about monarchs, migration, and metamorphosis into any number of directions, investigating through individual internet research and observation or with the help of other citizen scientists in and outside of the classroom. Hopefully an important part of what students can gain from this unit will be a sense that seeking truth and meaning can happen in so many different ways, but it certainly does not have to be isolated or isolating.

On the Web

- Journey North (*www.learner.org/jnorth*): An online science education project in which students track wildlife migration and seasonal change, following organisms ranging from monarch butterflies to gray whales

- Monarch Watch (*www.monarchwatch.org*): A network of students, teachers, other citizen scientists and researchers dedicated to the study of the monarch butterfly

- Monarch Larva Monitoring Project (*www.mlmp.org*): A citizen science project aiming to better understand how and why monarch populations vary in time and space, with a focus on distribution and abundance during the breeding season in North America

- The Monarch Monitoring Project (*www.monarchmonitoringproject.com*): A research and education program focusing on the fall migration of monarch butterflies along the Atlantic coast

Additional Resources

Berkes, M., and J. DiRubbio. 2010. *Going home: The mystery of animal migration*. Nevada City, CA: Dawn Publications.
Summary: A picture book with poems and factual information about a variety of migrating animals

Halpern, S. 2002. *Four wings and a prayer: Caught in the mystery of the Monarch Butterfly.* New York: Vintage Books.
Summary: A journalist's quest to understand the butterflies and the scientists who investigate them

Chapter 6

Case Study: Amphibians and Reptiles

by Terry M. Tomasek

I really do not remember an experience with a reptile or amphibian [herp] when I was little. I will have to say that my first actual encounter with a herp was Monday's frog call walk [June 21, 2010]. Catching the first Fowler's Toad of the night was pretty amazing but the best thing was probably seeing a full-grown Fowler's Toad. While everyone was trying to catch a frog somewhere else I moved away from all the noise and crowd and suddenly, walking in a new direction, I saw the toad. It was sitting so still and so calm on top of a small rock and then I started to think to myself "these herps are wonderful, peaceful creatures, which we humans have been harming, and yet they try so hard to avoid us." I was pointing the flashlight at this toad, and it was not calling but its vocal sac was blowing in and out of its throat. I did not try to catch it because I wanted to admire it and picture it in my head all the different characteristics of the toad. Such as their wonderful permeable skin, the toad's three warts on each spot and definitely their metamorphic changes. Since they are small and warty looking creatures, normal people do not take the time to learn about them as they would if it was a puppy or rabbit. In reality learning about herpetofauna, especially amphibians, can tell us so much about all the wrong things we humans are doing to the environment.

—Araceli Morales-Santos, High School Student

It is hard to believe the 16-year old quoted above could not recall a time in her young life when she had encountered a frog, lizard, turtle, or salamander. In today's world, youth are spending less and less time exploring natural settings, and many are unaware of wildlife common in their own yards or communities. To counteract this trend, over the past five years we have conducted a citizen science herpetology program for high school students in North Carolina. We introduced them to these elusive organisms, their habitats, and connections to the global environment in connection with the North American Amphibian Monitoring Program (NAAMP). In this citizen science project, scientists correlate calling survey data with other variables to track amphibian population trends.

Through such efforts, our students have listened for frog and toad calls, determined abundance, and noted atmospheric conditions and habitat characteristics. These activities have broadened their ideas of what it means to conduct scientific investigations and deepened their sense of the importance of accurate data collection. Students also have grown to see themselves as scientists with contributions to make in their community and beyond.

Calling surveys are most applicable in eastern and northern parts of North America, where many species regularly vocalize and have breeding seasons that extend over several weeks. In the west, calling surveys are less useful because the species call infrequently or quietly.

Calling Amphibian Surveys

Before participating in NAAMP amphibian surveys, volunteers use an online quiz to practice and demonstrate proficiency in recognizing calls of frogs and toads in their state. Participants drive along specified routes during breeding season. At each stop, they listen for five minutes, tally the frog and toad species they have heard, and estimate the abundance of each species. An abundance index of "1" means that individuals can be counted with space between calls, "2" indicates that individual calls can be distinguished but with some overlap, and "3" refers to a full chorus in which calls are constant, continuous, and overlapping.

Our students used species detection maps from the NAAMP website to generate lists of calling amphibians common to our community. Using photos and online recordings, they learned how to identify local species that were calling in the current season. The next step was to take a frog call hike based on NAAMP protocols that we had modified a bit for student use. Our goal was to inventory the calling amphibian species on the school property and determine the abundance index for each. We shortened our survey route to make it possible to walk rather than drive, and we decreased the number of stops and the amount of time spent at each (see Lesson 12, "Who's Out There? A Calling Amphibian Survey," for sampling details and data sheets). At each stop, students noted which species they had heard, agreed on an index of abundance, and recorded the temperature and moon phase.

In follow-up discussion, students expressed surprise and excitement about hearing the frogs, and they were highly engaged in discussing the limitations of this type of investigation. They identified biasing agents such as observer error in call identification and pointed out the challenge presented when one species' call interferes with detection of other quieter species. They noted that their ability to differentiate or count individuals declined with increasing numbers of frogs or toads, and they recognized limits in accuracy of the index of abundance due to this bias associated with call saturation. Another weakness that students pointed out was the relative ease of detecting large populations compared with smaller ones. Conducting this investigation made students aware of the complex nature of science. The field survey also awakened their awareness of amphibian calls in their everyday environment, and they mentioned with excitement that they had begun hearing frogs around their homes that they had never before noticed.

Aquatic Turtle and Box Turtle Mark-and-Recapture Studies

Students used baited traps to conduct mark-and-recapture investigations of aquatic turtle populations in a nearby 13 acre lake. They recorded the types of turtles captured and estimated their population sizes. They also investigated questions such as whether trap location or bait type might affect the types and numbers of turtles captured, or whether camouflaged traps would capture more turtles than non-camouflaged ones. We have been conducting the aquatic turtle investigation for over six years, and each year students continue to develop new questions.

Once traps were pulled from the lake, students identified the species that had been captured and then weighed, measured, and photographed each turtle (Figure 6.1). Before releasing them back into the lake, we tagged each turtle using a triangular file to mark an individualized three-letter code in the top shell edge (Figure 6.2).

FIGURE 6.1.

Students measuring a turtle

FIGURE 6.2.

Aquatic turtle tagged through notching of the shell

Back in the classroom, students entered their data into spreadsheets. Since this has been a long-term investigation, students have the opportunity to analyze data that have been collected for a number of years by previous classes. To address our initial question of what turtle species are found in the lake, each year we used the entire multiyear data set to create a species list and determine the gender ratio, the size range within each species, and the number of captures and recaptures. We used the following Lincoln-Petersen Index formula to determine a population estimate for each species.

$$N = \left[\frac{(n + 1)\,(M + 1)}{R + 1} \right] - 1$$

where:

N = estimate of total population size

M = number of animals marked in first sample

n = total animals captured in second sample (marked and unmarked)

R = number of recaptures in second sample

As students "messed around" with the data, they began to ask new questions such as:

- Which trap placement was most successful during a trapping season?

- How much has a turtle grown over the course of the current data set?

- How large an area in the lake has a single turtle been using?

- What is the relationship between plastron length and weight for a particular turtle species?

- Does usage of the lake vary with turtle species?

- Is there a correlation between trap success and recreational use of the lake?

Beginning with their question and a review of the data, each student stated a scientific claim, making an assertion that addressed their question. Students then had to describe the evidence that they were using to support their claim. We taught that authentic scientific argument

1. presents a potential explanation for the phenomenon of interest,

2. uses data as evidence to support the explanation,

3. acknowledges any other possible explanations that would fit the data, and

4. describes if and how the initial model of the phenomenon should change in light of the evidence.

We found that students were highly engaged in this important aspect of science, mainly because they were working with their own data within the context of a broader study.

Box Turtle Mark and Recapture

Students conducted a similar mark-and-recapture study with the terrestrial eastern box turtle (genus *Terrapene*) at a nearby nature center to address questions about populations and ranges. Our class used Boykin Spaniel dogs trained to find box turtles. When the dogs found a turtle, the site was marked with flagging tape and the location was recorded with GPS. Turtles were processed in a similar fashion to the aquatic turtles described above, with notches filed and morphometric data collected. In some cases, a turtle was fitted with a radio transmitter before being released at the point of capture. Students used radio telemetry equipment to find these turtles at a later date and record their new locations. The box turtles were tracked multiple times during the year. (See Lesson 11, "Turtle Trackers," for further ideas about student investigations of local turtles, both aquatic and terrestrial.)

Other Types of Survey Projects

We have worked with students on several other types of habitat-specific surveys for amphibians and reptiles. These included coverboard transects and drift fence pit traps in woodland habitat and leaf packs in streams. We also have used minnow traps to conduct population surveys in ephemeral pools (Figure 6.3), which

FIGURE 6.3.

Students identifying organisms at an ephemeral pool

provide excellent breeding grounds for amphibians because they dry out during parts of the year and therefore do not support fish populations. (See Lesson 13, "Wetland Discovery," for more ideas about ephemeral pool studies).

Citizen Science Participation

Our amphibian surveys and turtle investigations were conducted as part of student participation in the Carolina Herp Atlas citizen science project. This project documents the occurrence of amphibians and reptiles in North and South Carolina. The website provides distribution maps, charts, tables, photographs, and links to more detailed information. Registered users keep a personal database and employ a variety of data visualization tools to explore species diversity. At the end of each turtle sampling event, one student would sign in for the class and upload the group's data. Students also were encouraged to create their own personal Herp Atlas accounts so that they could continue uploading any data collected on their own, beyond our class activities. Over time, students were indeed finding amphibians and reptiles in their neighborhoods and submitting these observations to their own Herp Atlas accounts.

Students discovered that scientists use the Carolina Herp Atlas database to understand activity periods, habitat relationships, and current distributions of reptiles and amphibians, and that government agencies use it to make better decisions about conservation of our natural heritage. One group of students reviewed a state-level reptile and amphibian field guide to make a list of species likely to be found in the county where they lived. They then went to the Carolina Herp Atlas to see what species had been recorded for their county. To their dismay, very little data had been entered. Deciding that they wanted to do something about this, these students initiated a project to document all species of amphibians and reptiles in their county. They communicated with the Collections Manager for Herpetology at the State Museum of Natural Sciences to coordinate their efforts to submit data to the Herp Atlas, and they provided needed voucher specimens for the museum. Engaging in citizen science during class was the spark that lit the fire under these budding scientists!

On the Web

- Carolina Herp Atlas (*www.carolinaherpatlas.org*): A citizen science project that is assembling data on the distribution of reptiles and amphibians in North and South Carolina

- North American Amphibian Monitoring Program (NAAMP) (*www.pwrc.usgs.gov/naamp*): A nationwide citizen science project in which volunteers help states and USGS to assess frog and toad population trends, identifying local amphibian species using their unique breeding vocalizations or calls

- USGS Frog Call Website (*www.pwrc.usgs.gov/frogquiz*): Quizzes and a look-up function make it possible to learn the breeding calls of frogs and toads in the eastern United States and Canada

Additional Resources

Somers, A. B., and C. E. Matthews. 2003. Outdoor adventures: Tracking Eastern Box Turtles. *Science Scope* 27 (3): 32–37.
Summary: Describes turtle tracking by middle school students

Tomasek, T. M., C. E. Matthews, and J. Hall. 2005. What's slithering around on your school grounds? *American Biology Teacher* 67 (7): 419–425.
Summary: Provides details about surveying amphibian and reptile diversity using artificial cover, drift fences with pitfall and funnel traps, PVC pipes, and aquatic minnow traps

Chapter 7

An Integrative Approach to Studying Our Changing Planet

by Nancy M. Trautmann

Birds, butterflies, frogs and toads ... Chapters 4, 5, and 6 describe various approaches to studying individual species or taxonomic groups. This chapter takes a more integrative approach, delving into ecological interactions and responses to environmental change. The tremendous growth in natural history monitoring through citizen science has created exciting opportunities for students to become involved in real scientific investigations of tremendous importance to life on Earth, for example addressing impacts of climate change, spread of invasive species, and efforts to protect threatened species or habitats.

Climate Change

Each spring, plants leaf out and bloom, insects emerge, frogs reawaken from dormant states, and many bird species migrate between their wintering and breeding grounds. Relationships between climate and seasonal biological phenomena such as these are the focus of a science called phenology. With warming climate, some plants have begun blooming earlier in the spring, and some species of insects that feed on the nectar or pollen are adapting by altering the timing of their spring emergence. However, not all species are reacting in the same way or at the same rate. In some cases, these differences are disrupting key synchronies between species. For example, many bird species migrate north to breed because of the more abundant supply of insects available there to feed their young, and they may be unable to change their nesting dates to coincide with earlier emergence of key insect populations. Similarly, if insect pollinators emerge outside the window of time in which their target species of flowers are blooming, the insects miss the nectar and the plants miss this chance for pollen dispersal.

To track broadscale phenological change across the globe, researchers increasingly rely on monitoring conducted by citizen scientists. For example, the National Phenology Network maintains the Nature's Notebook database to keep track of biological signals of environmental change among a large assortment of plant and animal species. Data collected in recent years have documented early leaf-out in northern forests in response to unusually warm winters and springs. Students can join with professional scientists, policy makers, and resource managers in using such data to explore how plants and animals are responding to environmental change, predict long-term impacts, and consider possible mitigating action for protection of threatened species or ecosystems.

In Lesson 8, "Winter Twig Investigation," students track the progression of twig and blossom development in a selected plant species and compare this with data reported to Project Budburst by other citizen scientists. In Lesson 9, "Flight of the Pollinators: Plant Phenology From a Pollinator's Perspective," students explore connections between timing of blossoming and life cycles of the insects or birds that rely on these blossoms for food. In Lesson 6, "Bird Migration Patterns in My Area," they discover which birds in their area migrate and which do not and use eBird data to explore whether any changes are apparent in the dates of arrival or departure of selected species. In Lesson 4, "Signs of Spring: Earthworm Inquiry," students use Journey North to track signs of spring based on first sightings of earthworms as they complete their vertical migration from the soil depths back to the surface of the ground. Combining a variety of lessons such as these could build a more holistic view of impacts of climate change in a selected geographic setting.

Not only individual species, but entire habitats are affected by climate change. Ephemeral pools dry up each year and accommodate species accustomed to such annual cycles. But what happens in times of unusual heat and drought, or seasons that remain unusually wet and cold? Can the species that have adapted to typical annual wet/dry cycles survive these extremes? In Lesson 13, "Wetland Discovery," students learn about the ecological importance of temporary bodies of water and conduct fieldwork to map and inventory species in a wetland of this type in their community.

Invasive Species

The spread of invasive species is a major factor causing ecosystem change throughout the world. Ranging from microorganisms to large mammals, invasives have the ability to displace or eradicate native species, alter landscapes, and cause huge economic losses. Citizen science provides a potent tool for tracking the appearance and advance of invasive species. Spread of the Eurasian collared-dove across the United States, for example, was documented through sightings reported to Project FeederWatch (Figure 7.1).

Tracking the spread of an invasive species is one potential focus for student investigations. Another option is to explore potential impacts of such introductions on native species that may be outcompeted for food, shelter, and other resources. House sparrows, European starlings, and rock doves (commonly called pigeons) are among the most common and abundant bird species in North America. All three are nonnative species that were introduced into the United States in the 1800s and quickly spread across the continent. House Sparrows are well adapted to living under a wide range of conditions, urban as well as rural, but in some areas they appear to be outcompeted by house finches (Cornell Lab of Ornithology 2011). Is this the case in your community? How does house sparrow abundance compare with abundance of selected native species such as the American tree sparrow? Or consider European starlings—these birds nest in cavities and compete with native cavity nesters such as the eastern bluebird. Is their huge abundance affecting the populations of bluebirds or other native species? Using online data from eBird and other citizen science projects, students can pose questions such as these and explore relationships among the presence and abundance of selected species of interest (see Lesson 6, "Bird Migration Patterns in My Area").

Rare and Endangered Species

FIGURE 7.1.

The spread of an invasive species across the country

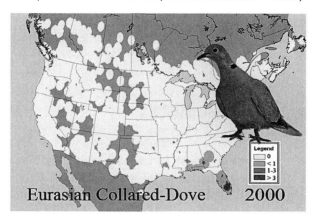

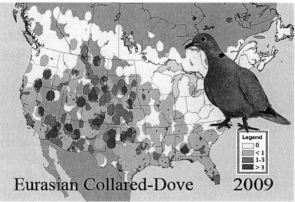

Source: Project FeederWatch

One of the goals of natural history monitoring is to keep common species common by noticing downward trends before it is too late to take preventative action. Another goal is to inventory key habitats in order to target these areas for protection. When scientists realized in 2008 that the populations of once-common rusty blackbirds had plummeted for unknown reasons, they put out a special call for birders across North America to submit sightings of this species, stating: "Working together we hope to determine the cause and come up with management solutions before the species joins the growing ranks of the threatened and endangered" (Greenberg 2008).

The Lost Ladybug Project focuses on both rare and invasive species by tracking trends in the distribution of North American ladybug species. Over the past 20 years, several native ladybugs that once were common have become rare, while nonnative ladybug populations have expanded in numbers and range. According to the project scientists, "This is happening very quickly and we don't know how, or why, or what impact it will have on ladybug diversity or the role that ladybugs play in keeping plant-feeding insect populations low. We're asking you to join us in finding out where all the ladybugs have gone so we can try to prevent more native species from becoming so rare" (Lost Ladybug Project 2012).

Aquatic Habitats

Water is an integrating force, tying together through the water cycle all parts of our environment, but school classes that monitor streams in noncoastal locations may not think to relate their findings to potential impacts on life in the ocean. Lesson 14, "Using Inland and Costal Citizen Science Opportunities to Study Marine Food Webs," makes this connection between watersheds and marine food webs, using citizen science and real or virtual field trips to familiarize students with connections between what we do on land and how it affects organisms in both freshwater and marine environments. Impacts of human activities and land use management on aquatic life are also addressed in Lesson 13, "Wetland Discovery," in this case focusing on life in ephemeral wetlands. These temporary water bodies may look like nothing but big puddles that seasonally become dry, but in fact they represent critical habitat to a variety of rare species, including amphibians and insects specially adapted to thrive in these harsh conditions. Lesson 11, "Turtle Trackers," and Lesson 12, "Who's Out There? A Calling Amphibian Survey," also relate to wetland wildlife, focusing on turtles, frogs, and toads and the need for conservation of their aquatic habitats.

Biodiversity

You may have heard of "BioBlitzes." These intensive 24-hour events aim to inventory as many species of plants, animals, microbes, fungi, and other organisms as possible within a designated area and create a snapshot in time. The University of Connecticut conducts biannual BioBlitzes in celebration of the diversity of life in familiar neighborhood habitats: "We hear again and again about the negative impacts we've had on biodiversity such as the loss of species and the destruction of habitats. It seems rare to accentuate and celebrate something positive. The BioBlitz is a chance to highlight the positive impact that city parks and open spaces, with all their diversity, have on our everyday lives" (University of Connecticut 2012). The aim is educational as well as scientific:

We usually hear the word "biodiversity" in regard to rainforests with their vast number of species. Yet the diversity of life in our own backyards is phenomenal. We take for granted clean water, fertile soil, and air to breathe. Yet these are all the result of working ecosystems filled with species that perform these tasks. From our morning shower to our late night snack, we are supported by biodiversity every minute of the day. What better way to address the topic than to invite people to share in our 24-hours of discovery and to experience the vast array of species that we can find in their neighborhood park in just one cycle of the day? (University of Connecticut 2012)

Even if no organization will be hosting a BioBlitz in your community, you and your students can hold your own school yard event (National Geographic 2012).

Another option is to inventory terrestrial invertebrates in local soil samples and submit the data to the Hands on the Land website (see Lesson 3, "Terrestrial Invertebrates"). This citizen science project is hosted by Great Smoky Mountains National Park, where a huge effort is underway to try to identify all forms of life within the park. This "All Taxa Biodiversity Inventory" includes soil invertebrates and has resulted in discovery of some species previously unknown to science (Repanshek 2007)! The Terrestrial Invertebrate Study allows students to get involved, either in the park or in your own school yard or community.

Conducting a species inventory gives students practice in using a dichotomous key, recording data, and mapping. Analyzing data collected over time or across sites offers opportunities to investigate questions on topics such as adaptations, habitats, population dynamics, and human impacts. Students could compare terrestrial invertebrate biodiversity in two or more soil locations, for example, contrasting life found beneath a manicured lawn with that in a wildflower meadow. Which habitat supports a greater variety and abundance of soil invertebrates? What changes occur over time if an area is left unmowed and allowed to revert to a more wild state? Students also can manipulate data on the Hands on the Land website, producing charts or graphs to explore relationships between invertebrate diversity or abundance and environmental variables such as soil or air temperature, soil pH, cloud cover, precipitation, and canopy cover.

Another approach to studying biodiversity is to monitor species before and after taking steps to improve habitat. In the YardMap project, students can join with other citizen scientists in mapping such improvements and sharing strategies taken to create better habitat and attract a richer diversity of bird life to school yards, parks, and other open spaces (see Lesson 7, "Habitat Matters: YardMap Your School Yard!").

Conclusion

Whether you elect to focus on individual species or entire ecosystems, your students can conduct fascinating and useful investigations in your own community that will contribute to ecological understandings on a broader scale. Through citizen science, students can analyze real data, whether or not they collect it themselves, and address crucial scientific questions on topics such as biodiversity, climate change, invasive species, and conservation of endangered species or habitats. We hope that these chapters and the following lesson plans will inspire you to join the ever-growing legions of citizen scientists in the United States and across the globe who collectively are changing the face of science and conducting monitoring and research at previously unimaginable scales.

On the Web

- eBird (*http://ebird.org*): A citizen science project that collects and displays data about birds around the world

- Hands on the Land (*www.handsontheland.org*): A national network of field classrooms and agency resources to connect people with public lands and waterways

- Journey North (*www.learner.org/jnorth*): A citizen science project that engages students in tracking wildlife migration and seasonal change

- Lost Ladybug Project (*www.lostladybug.org*): A citizen science project that documents ladybug abundance across North America

- Nature's Notebook (*www.usanpn.org/home*): A project that gathers information on plant and animal phenology across the United States

- Project Budburst (*http://neoninc.org/budburst*): A citizen science project that collects data about plant phenology

- Project FeederWatch (*www.birds.cornell.edu/pfw*): A citizen science project that collects and displays data on feeder birds in the United States and Canada

- YardMap (*www.yardmap.org*): A citizen science project that collects habitat data and provides information about sustainable landscapes

References

Cornell Lab of Ornithology. 2011. When invasive species clash: Competition between the House Sparrow and House Finch. *Project FeederWatch Blog* (March 10). *http://*

projectfeederwatch.wordpress.com/2011/03/10/when-invasive-species-clash-competition-between-the-house-sparrow-and-house-finch

Greenberg, R. 2008. The decline and fall of the Rusty Blackbird. Help monitor this vulnerable species by reporting your sightings. *The great backyard bird count. www.birdsource.org/gbbc/science-stories/past-stories/the-decline-and-fall-of-the-rusty-blackbird*

Lost Ladybug Project. 2012. Welcome to the Lost Ladybug Project. *www.lostladybug.org*

National Geographic. 2012. BioBlitz education: Field learning resources. *http://education.nationalgeographic.com/education/program/bioblitz/?ar_a=1*

Repanshek, K. 2007. Biodiversity studies in the parks reveal previously unknown species. *National Parks Traveler* (September 24). *www.nationalparkstraveler.com/2007/09/biodiversity-studies-parks-reveal-previously-unknown-species*

University of Connecticut. 2012. Bioblitz: Celebrate with us. *http://web.uconn.edu/mnh/bioblitz*

L E S S O N 1

Whale Song Project

by Debra Taylor Hall, North Carolina Department of Public Instruction

Overview

Students classify whale calls in an online database in order to assist scientists in understanding behavioral responses of killer and pilot whales to sonar and other loud sounds in the ocean.

Learning Objectives

Students will be able to:

- Analyze and interpret a spectrogram and match it to the sound that it represents

- Describe effects of underwater noise on whale communication and behavior

- Explain the role of citizen science in research and policy-setting related to noise in the ocean

Big Idea

Whales use sound to communicate with each other, and their ability to communicate is affected by natural and human-made ocean sounds.

Citizen Science Connection

The Whale Song Project (*www.whale.fm*)

Time Required/Location

Three 45-minute periods, indoors

1

Resources Needed

- Computer with internet access and speakers for class demonstrations of whale songs

- Cards for card-sort activity (see Figure 1.1, p. 64)

- Computer lab with enough stations for students to work individually or in small groups

- Headphones for each student in the computer lab

- Interactive whiteboard or computer projector helpful but not required

Background Information

Killer whales, also known as orcas, communicate with each other through sound. Each family group has its own dialect, and closely related families share calls. Pilot Whales also communicate vocally and have dialects, but less is known about their communication patterns. Whales use sound to find food, orient themselves, stay in contact with others, and navigate. Noise from the engines of tankers and other large ships can startle whales and disrupt their feeding and communication. Extremely loud underwater noise can even lead to hearing loss and other serious physical injury of whales and other marine organisms. Air guns used in undersea oil exploration can cause this sort of disruption, as can sonar used for tracking submarines and torpedoes.

In the Whale Song Project, citizen scientists listen to and categorize online recordings of whale calls to group similar-sounding calls together and help scientists determine whether the same type of call is made by a single whale, a group in close proximity, or whales spread across broad regions of the sea. Such research is leading to better understanding of whale communication patterns and can be used in tailoring regulations to protect vital functions of marine life.

Conducting the Activity

Engage

1. Use a formative assessment card sort to have students classify items into two categories: organisms that use sound to communicate, and organisms that do NOT use sound to communicate (see Figure 1.1, p. 64).

2. Organize students into small groups and ask them to discuss the cards and place each into one of the two categories. Listen to their reasoning for the

classification and note misconceptions and instructional opportunities to challenge these ideas.

Explore

1. Listen to a variety of whale songs from websites such as those listed in the On the Web section.

2. Have students draw illustrations representing one or more selected vocalizations. For example, they might choose to draw high and low notes on a graph or a musical score, or to draw a series of lines going up and down to represent their view of the sounds they are hearing.

3. Discuss the sounds and visual representations made by the students. Identify patterns in the vocalizations and discuss how these are represented in the drawings.

4. Using the tutorial and the "About/Background" section on the Whale Song Project website (*www.whale.fm/tutorial*), introduce the Whale FM citizen science project. Ask students, "What is citizen science, and how does it relate to whale song?"

   Citizen science *refers to efforts in which volunteers partner with professional scientists to collect or analyze data. Through the Whale Song Project, citizen scientists contribute to whale communication research by listening to calls and pairing each call with another that provides the closest match. This sorting helps researchers to categorize complex calls and try to determine the meaning of various types of whale vocalizations. See Chapter 1, "What Is Citizen Science?" for more information.*

5. As a group, listen to a sound from the website, observe the provided spectrograms, and select the most suitable match.

   The "Help" section of the website models the process of matching whale calls. When you find a potentially matching call, click its checkmark and that call will be enlarged and displayed next to the main sound on the page. You can then compare these two sounds more closely and either select another or click "MATCH" to confirm this choice. Each matching pair is recorded in the project database, and then a new main sound is displayed along with another set of potential matches.

6. Working individually or in small groups, have students create free accounts on the project website. Ask them to select a particular type of whale or region of the world and conduct some matches on their own by clicking on the provided spectrogram to hear the associated whale call and following the same procedure you modeled as a class.

Explain

1. Compare the illustrations that students drew in Step 2 of the Explore section with spectrograms of these same sounds. Did anyone draw visualization similar to a spectrogram?

2. Discuss with students how a spectrogram represents sound. You might wish to use the examples on the Listen for Whales website to walk through several whale calls and learn how to read the spectrogram for each.

   A spectrogram is a graph that represents sound visually, with pitch along the y-axis and time across the x-axis.

3. Ask students what changes they hear when playing a recording at faster or slower than normal speed, and how these changes would be reflected in spectrograms.

   When sped up, sounds move to a higher pitch. Spectrogram images for these higher pitches would extend farther up the y-axis, and the faster speed at which the sound is played would reduce the length of the image along the x-axis.

Elaborate

1. Ask students to read the "About/Science" section of the Whale Song Project website or other sources such as Broad (2012) and BRP (2013).

2. Discuss as a class why scientists are conducting the WhaleFM project. What kinds of natural and human-made phenomena produce sound underwater? How are whales affected by these sounds? Ask students to think about the frustration of trying to listen to a phone conversation when a noisy truck rumbles by (or simulate this activity), and relate this experience to communication among whales being blocked by ship traffic or other underwater noise.

Researchers are studying the effect of sound on the behavior of marine mammals to learn how and why these organisms respond to various sound stimuli. This information is needed in order to design regulations and guidelines to reduce the impact of noise produced by sonar blasts, ship traffic, oil and gas exploration, and other human activities on communication among whales and other forms of marine life.

3. As a class, discuss how scientists collect whale song data and why it is difficult to analyze these data without the help of citizen science volunteers.

    Focus on the vast amount of information that has been collected in acoustic data sets and the amount of time it would take a few people to categorize all of these sounds. It would not be feasible for individual scientists to analyze and interpret the many hours of ocean acoustic data. Citizen scientists' efforts to sort whale calls into categories enable researchers to focus on data of greatest relevance to each question of interest.

4. After reading the "About/Science" section of the project website, ask why some of the calls remain a mystery to scientists.

    Discuss the idea that we do not know enough about whale communication but hope to learn more by examining these data. Scientists know that whales use contact calls to find each other and to seek mates, but many of the specific calls remain a mystery. Communication by killer whales and pilot whales is still poorly understood, and more needs to be learned about why and when they make specific calls.

Evaluate

1. Have students create a podcast describing the impacts of human activities on the ability of whales to communicate, supporting their argument with evidence from the Whale Song Project website and other resources such as those listed below.

2. Have students write an article for a local newspaper about their experience as a citizen scientist. Instruct them to include:

    *   A sample spectrogram and brief explanation of what it portrays,

- Description of why citizen science is important in whale communication research and policy setting, and

- Explanation of potential impacts of excess underwater noise on whales.

  Optional: Have students exchange articles and provide peer review. After revisions are made, mask the authors' names and have the class vote on the best articles to send to the editor of the local paper for potential publication.

Extend

1. Through the Listen for Whales project, learn how acoustical monitoring in the ocean near Boston is helping to protect the world's last 350 North Atlantic right whales, and follow this work real-time in late spring or view archives of a previous whale migration season.

2. Using the Don't be a Buckethead website, explore the effects of noise pollution in the ocean on marine animals and fish.

3. The Sea of Sound curriculum offers eight standards-based classroom activities for biology in grades 7 to 12 and physics courses, including "Seeing Sound" and "Listen for Whales," along with free sound analysis software and animal sound files (Rice 2011).

Lesson Resource

- Cards for card-sort activity: Create cards using a variety of terms or pictures such as those shown in Figure 1.1 (p. 64).

On the Web

- Don't be a Buckethead (*http://dontbeabuckethead.org*): Activities and background information about human-caused ocean noise and how it affects marine life

- Listen for Whales (*www.listenforwhales.org*): Near real-time detection of Right Whale calls to protect this highly endangered species from collisions with ships along the Atlantic coast

- Macaulay Library of Animal Audio and Video Recordings (*http://macaulaylibrary.org*): Cornell Lab of Ornithology's scientific archive of audio and video recordings for a huge range of animal species

- National Oceanographic and Atmospheric Administration (NOAA), A Collection of Sounds from the Sea (*http://oceanexplorer.noaa.gov/explorations/sound01/background/ seasounds/ seasounds.html#big*): Spectrograms and sound files of recordings of a variety of undersea sounds from earthquakes, volcanic tremors, ships, air guns, and whales

- Victoria Experimental Network Under the Sea (*http://venus.uvic.ca/multimedia-features/ hydrophone-highlights/ship-sounds*): Spectrograms and sound files of recordings of a variety of ships in the Strait of Georgia, a busy shipping channel

- Whales, Dolphins, and Sound (*www.environment.gov.au/coasts/species/cetaceans/ sound.html*): Australian government site that provides example whale songs and describes the importance of sound to whales and dolphins for hunting, navigating and communicating

References

Bioaccoustics Research Program (BRP). 2013. *Effects of human-made sound on the behavior of whales. www.birds.cornell.edu/brp/research/effects-of-human-made-sound-on-the-behavior-of-whales*

Broad, W. J. 2012. A rising tide of noise is now easy to see. *New York Times* (December 10).

Rice, E. 2011. Sea of sound. *www.birds.cornell.edu/Page.aspx?pid=2207*

FIGURE 1.1.

Example cards for use in the card-sort activity

Organisms that use sound to communicate	Organisms that do NOT use sound to communicate

Whales	Frogs	Trees	Spiders
Birds	Mushrooms	Insects	Jellyfish
Dogs	Bees	Worms	Alligators

LESSON

It's Been a Hard Day's Flight

Determining Daily Flight Distances of Monarch Butterflies

by Heather Brubach, Penn-Alexander School, Philadelphia

Overview

Students learn about the migratory patterns of monarch butterflies and explore tagging recovery data from the Monarch Watch citizen science project. They calculate average flight distances, make claims about their findings, look critically at these claims, and adjust claims if needed based on additional evidence. This data analysis lesson can stand alone or complement projects in which students raise or tag monarchs (see Chapter 5, "Case Study: The Mysteries of Monarchs").

Learning Objectives

Students will be able to:

- Estimate the average rate of travel for monarch butterflies based on data from Monarch Watch

- Calculate averages using multiple sets of data

- Understand that sample size has significant impact on the credibility of a claim

- Interpret data on a scatter plot graph

Big Idea

The credibility of scientific claims about the world around us depends on the amount and type of data and evidence used to support them.

Citizen Science Connection

- Monarch Watch (*www.MonarchWatch.org*)
- Journey North (*www.learner.org/jnorth/ monarch*)

Time Required/Location

90–120 minutes, indoors

Resources Needed

- Computer with iinternet access

- Projector or interactive whiteboard

- Large chart paper and markers

- PBS/Nova video: The Incredible Journey of the Butterflies, available online: (*http://video.pbs.org/video/1063682334*)

- Small dot stickers

- 1 red marker

- 1 green marker

- Copy or image of Monarch Recovery Data Table to project or share with the class

- Monarch data for each pair of students (see Instructions for Preparing Data from the Monarch Watch Recovery Database)

- Calculators

- Student Claim Worksheet

Background Information

Monarch butterflies conduct amazing migratory flights stretching up to 3,000 miles from their summer breeding grounds in the United States to winter roosting spots. Those west of the Rocky Mountains fly to small groves of trees along the California coast, and those in the eastern United States fly all the way to Mexico, where they congregate in huge clusters in forests high in the mountains. They are the only butterflies anywhere in the world to make such a long, two-way migration every year. Migration is triggered by seasonal changes in day length and temperature. Several generations of monarchs are produced each summer. Adults that emerge from the final generation in the fall look like summer adults but don't mate or lay eggs until after migrating south for the winter and back north the following spring. As monarchs migrate up to 3,000 miles southward, they stop to feed on nectar that will build fat stores to carry them through the winter months. They are cold-blooded and unable to fly if the weather gets too cold.

Monarch tagging and recovery helps scientists track monarch migrations to learn when they travel and how fast, how far, and where they go. It also helps with research into the great mysteries underlying how these fragile insects can survive such long flights, find distant overwintering sites they have never seen, and pass along crucial information to future generations who will make the same journeys for the first time after emerging from eggs laid by adults who have lived only a brief time and never migrated.

Conducting the Activity

Engage

1. Introduce the migration of monarch butterflies by showing the first two minutes of the video, "The Incredible Journey of the Butterflies" (http://video.pbs.org/video/1063682334).

2. Consider engaging students' interest in monarchs by having them tag or even raise and tag monarch butterflies (see Chapter 5, "Case Study: The Mysteries of Monarchs").

3. Briefly introduce the Monarch Watch citizen science project (*www.monarchwatch.org*) and its procedures for tagging and recovery of monarchs. Ask students, "What is citizen science?"

   Citizen science *refers to efforts in which volunteers partner with professional scientists to collect or analyze data. Through the Monarch Watch Project, citizen scientists help scientists by tagging migrating monarch butterflies and reporting recovered tag information. The recovery data are posted online for use by students and professional scientists in analyzing monarch orientation and navigation. See Chapter 1 ("What Is Citizen Science?") for more information.*

4. Ask: What are some variables that might affect the data in Monarch Watch?

   Seasons, weather, nonlinear migration patterns, etc. For more information, see www.monarchwatch.org/tagmig/recoveries.htm

5. Using the "Instructions for Preparing Data From the Monarch Watch Recovery Database" provided with this lesson (p. 73), bring up a Monarch Watch data table and share it with the class. Explain that each row reports the distance flown by an individual butterfly, and discuss what information you would use to convert this into the average distance flown per day by that individual.

See Figure 2.1 for example data. Average distance flown by each butterfly is calculated by dividing the total distance traveled by the number of days between tag date and recovery date for that individual.

Explore

1. Divide students into groups of two or three. Assign each group data from 10 butterflies to analyze. Explain that each group should determine the average distance traveled per day by each butterfly before it was recaptured.

2. Create a large class scatter plot graph, have students plot their butterflies' average distance/day by the number of days between tagging and recovery.

    See Figure 2.2 for an example graph.

FIGURE 2.1.

Example butterfly flight data from Monarch Watch

Tag Code	Tag City	Tag State	Tag Date	Report Date	Report City	Report State	Report Country	Miles
GEN520	Brighton	ON	09/15/05	03/08/06	Cerro Pelon		MX	2268
217LD	Buena Vista		10/27/94	03/31/95	Port Aransas	TX	US	420
382BR	Tonganoxie	KS	09/27/93	10/08/93	Abilene	TX	US	528
801KF	Hesper	IA	09/01/94	03/01/95	Anangueo		MX	1718
824KF	Hesper	IA	09/06/94	09/11/94	Dyersville	IA	US	77

Explain

1. Looking at the class scatter plot graph, encourage discussion about what trends are apparent.

    Data points for butterflies that traveled a short time before recovery are clumped together compared with points for those who traveled for longer periods. Some students may realize that the more days the butterflies traveled, the more reliable the average distance/day.

2. Ask students how they might determine an average distance per day for all the butterflies they have investigated. Have them predict the average distance per day for all the butterflies in the entire set analyzed by the class, and ask how confident they are in this prediction.

FIGURE 2.2.

Example scatter plot showing relationship between average distance traveled per day by monarch butterflies and the length of time between their tagging and recovery

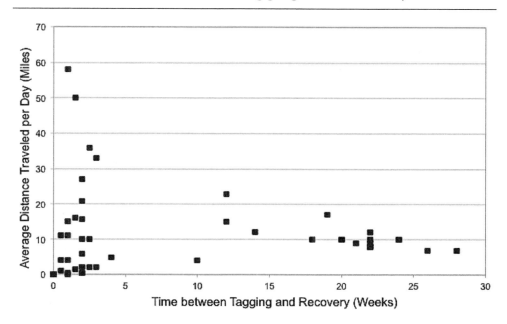

3. If students suggest taking the average of the averages, write down the average distance for each butterfly more clearly for all the class to see and have them do that calculation independently.

   The average distances are added together and divided by the number of butterflies.

4. After appropriate wait time, ask for a student to provide the solution and get agreement from the rest of the class. Then have a student come up and mark that average of averages on the graph by drawing a green horizontal line from that point on the *y*-axis. Encourage small-group discussion about this average and how it relates to the averages for each individual butterfly.

Elaborate

1. After a few minutes of discussion, come back together and ask students to share their thinking about how confident they are in using this calculation to

make a claim. Ask, does anyone know another, possibly better way, to determine the average distance/day of all the butterflies in the set? If students are having trouble thinking of another way, remind them to look at the data and axes on the graph.

Another way to calculate the average distance/day of all butterflies is to add all the total distances traveled and divide that by the total number of days traveled.

2. Have students assemble on a class chart the total number of days traveled and total distance traveled for each butterfly. Once this comprehensive data set has been assembled, have students recalculate the average distance traveled per day for the whole collection of butterflies in this class set.

3. Have a student state his or her solution to this calculation. After securing agreement from the class, have a volunteer draw a horizontal red line on the graph at the average distance that was obtained with this new calculation on the *y*-axis. Have students discuss with their group about how this new average compares with the average represented by the green line and with the individual averages that they plotted.

Evaluate

1. After a few minutes, ask students to think about and discuss which calculation produced a more accurate claim for the average distance traveled per day by this group of monarch butterflies. Ask them to explain their reasoning based on the data analyzed with the graph.

The second average (represented by the red line) is closer to the clumped averages of butterflies with more days traveled before recovery. It is a better overall average because it gives less weight to the less credible averages of butterflies that traveled fewer days before recovery.

2. Have each student complete the Student Claim Worksheet (p. 74). Collect this writing assignment as assessment for the activity.

Extend

1. Show the Tag Recovery data table you produced from the Monarch Watch website (such as Figure 2.1). Remind students that they looked at only a

small number of butterflies, compared with 16,157 individuals that have been recovered and entered into this database by volunteers all over North America. Discuss how citizen science allows scientists to have a larger sample size of butterfly data to study than they could possibly have obtained on their own. With such a vast amount of data to work with, scientists can make more reliable claims about monarch migration.

2. Compare the average distance/day that students calculated to the rate that the Monarch Watch scientists have posted using the much larger data set.

   See FAQ, Question 3, at www.monarchwatch.org/read/faq2.htm.

3. Have students brainstorm what else they could learn about monarchs by studying and analyzing the Monarch Watch recovery data. Ideas for related investigations could be possible independent research projects (for a science fair, for example), homework, or an extra credit assignment.

4. Follow monarch migration in real time during their spring or fall migration, and enter your own sightings of monarchs through the Journey North citizen science project.

5. Consider tagging monarchs, raising monarchs, and/or building butterfly gardens to help repair the fractured habitat and support the migration (see Chapter 5, "Case Study: The Mysteries of Monarchs").

Lesson Resources

- Instructions for Preparing Data From the Monarch Watch Recovery Database

- Student Claim Worksheet

On the Web

- MonarchLab (*www.monarchlab.org/Lab*): University of Minnesota provides a wealth of information about monarch biology, migration, and conservation, and tips on rearing them.

- Journey North (*www.learner.org/jnorth*): An online science education project in which students track wildlife migration and seasonal change, following organisms ranging from monarch butterflies to gray whales.

- Monarch Watch (*www.monarchwatch.org*): A network of students, teachers, other citizen scientists and researchers dedicated to the study of the monarch butterfly.

- Monarch Larva Monitoring Project (*www.mlmp.org*): A citizen science project aiming to better understand how and why monarch populations vary in time and space, with a focus on distribution and abundance during the breeding season in North America.

- The Monarch Monitoring Project (*www.monarchmonitoringproject.com*): A research and education program focusing on the fall migration of monarch butterflies along the Atlantic coast.

Instructions for Preparing Data From the Monarch Watch Recovery Database

Tags that are found are reported to the recovery database, which is a rich source of data that can be used for a variety of purposes. For this lesson, we recommend the following preparations to make data available to students.

Printing and Cutting Method

1. Go to the Migration and Tagging page: *www.monarchwatch.org/tagmig/recoveries.htm*

2. Click on Search the Monarch Tag Recovery Database.

3. Specify the following:

    • Minimum distance 30 miles

    • At the bottom "uncheck" tagger and reporter

4. Hit Submit.

5. This will yield a large set of data. Simply print as much of it as you need for your class(es) and cut the form into sections that will provide each pair or small group with a set of 10 recoveries.

6. Provide header information on the board or as a handout, as this will not be visible in the cut sections.

Card Method

Alternatively, you could prepare cards for each recovery, such as those below. These could, of course, be laminated and reused from year to year.

Monarch Data Card – Tag Code: AFM825

Tag Location: Goshen County, WY
Tag Date: 8/26/01
Distance Traveled: 1,538 Miles

Recovery Location: Sierra Chincua, MX
Recovery Date: 2/26/02

Monarch Data Card – Tag Code: 382BR

Tag Location: Tonganoxie, KS
Tag Date: 9/27/93
Distance Traveled: 523 Miles

Recovery Location: Abilene, TX
Recovery Date: 10/08/93

Student Claim Worksheet

Name:

1. State your claim about the average distance monarch butterflies fly in a day.

2. Give reasoning for your claim based on evidence from the Monarch Watch data analyzed.

3. How confident are you in your claim? Why?

4. Share any hesitations you feel, questions you still have, or further information you may want to feel more confident about your claim.

LESSON 3

Terrestrial Invertebrates

by Susan Sachs, Great Smoky Mountains National Park

Overview

Students engage in the scientific practices of collecting and analyzing biological inventory data. They analyze citizen science data to learn about terrestrial invertebrates and explore factors affecting their diversity, and they inventory terrestrial invertebrates on their school grounds or other site. This lesson is adapted from activities developed through the Parks as Classrooms project of Great Smoky Mountains National Park (Sachs, Absher, and Carmody 2011) and can be implemented in any part of the country.

Learning Objectives

Students will be able to:

- Identify and categorize a variety of terrestrial invertebrates to the taxonomic level of Order or Class

- Describe the role of invertebrates in food webs and their interdependence with plants, birds, and other taxonomic groups

- Interpret citizen science data, and make comparisons to address questions related to habitat needs and environmental change

Big Idea

Soil invertebrates make up an important but often overlooked component of terrestrial ecosystems. The diversity of invertebrates varies with season and with variables including soil pH, soil and air temperature, and type and extent of tree cover.

Citizen Science Connection

Hands on the Land, Terrestrial Invertebrate Study (*www.handsontheland.org/ environmental-monitoring/terrestrial-invertebrate-study.html*)

Time Required/Location

- Two 45-minute class period, indoors

- One 45-minute class period outdoors at minimum

Resources Needed

- Computer with internet access

- Interactive whiteboard or computer projector helpful

- Data sheets (1 per group)

- Clipboards (1 per group)

- Magnifying glasses (1 per group)

- Tweezers, eyedroppers, or small spoons for collecting invertebrates (1 per student)

- Jars or bug boxes (several per student)

- Terrestrial Invertebrate data sheet (1 per group)

- Additional apparatus recommended for biological inventory:

  o Thermometer

  o Soil thermometer

  o Soil pH probe

- Leaf litter sifter for collecting invertebrates (optional). Instructions on how to make the sifter can be found under Shaker Box Activity at *www.handsontheland.org/monitoring/projects/inverts/shaker_box_instructions.pdf*

Background Information

In Great Smoky Mountains National Park, a huge effort has been underway since 1998 to try to identify all forms of life within the Park. By the beginning of 2013, over 900 species had been found that are entirely new species to science, and approximately 80% of these are invertebrates, including new species of beetles, flies, spiders, moths, and butterflies (Nichols 2013). The Terrestrial Invertebrate Study is a citizen science project that allows students to get involved—in the Park, your school yard, or other site of your choice.

The biological inventory in this lesson involves exploring a site and developing a list of the types of soil invertebrates found. Conducting an inventory such as this produces baseline data that provides a standard against which you can compare change over time. Changes might occur in invertebrate populations due to soil erosion, air pollution, or other types of environmental change. Baseline data can have unanticipated uses as well. For example, in 2003, when educators in Great Smoky

Mountains National Park initiated a soil invertebrate citizen science project, they did not realize how useful the information collected by students would become in monitoring effects of climate change, particularly in the warmer spring months as invertebrates emerge earlier each year. The data set is proving useful in tracking changes in relationships between species, such as the timing of the emergence of invertebrates needed by plants for pollination or by birds to feed their young.

Conducting the Activity

Engage

1. Play the Biodiversity podcast video at *www.thegreatsmokymountains.org/ eft/10modules.html*. Turn the microscope knob on the computer screen to Section 1, Understanding Biodiversity and click "Watch Video." Although this video relates specifically to the Great Smoky Mountain National Park, it does a nice job of defining biodiversity and describing how geographical, geological, and atmospheric features contribute to biodiversity. It also provides an introduction to invertebrate diversity in the forest litter and suggests the value of inventory surveys and biological monitoring.

2. If you have access to a computer lab, you can also have students play the Bucket of Bugs game (*www.thegreatsmokymountains.org/eft/10modules.html*). Turn the microscope knob on the computer screen to Section 4, Studying Diversity. Click "Play Game" and follow instructions.

Explore

1. Select a study plot on or near your school property. Divide the students into groups and provide each group with collection equipment. One way in which to sample is to randomly toss hula hoops into the plot and have small groups of students survey organisms found in the leaf litter within each hoop. You could rely on a visual search for invertebrates or use a leaf litter sifter to collect them.

2. Have students work together to identify invertebrates to the Order or Class taxonomic level, and count the number of individuals within each group. A picture guide to soil invertebrates is available here, along with data sheets and other useful information at the Hands on the Land Terrestrial Invertebrates site. Release all insects back to the study site after they have been identified.

3. If you would like to define your own study site and enter the data into the Hands On the Land Terrestrial Invertebrates database, directions are provided in the Instructor's Guide available at the site. Data entry also includes soil temperature, air temperature, soil pH, cloud cover, precipitation, and percent canopy cover. Ask students, "What is citizen science?"

Citizen science refers to efforts in which volunteers partner with professional scientists to collect or analyze data. Through the Terrestrial Invertebrate Project, citizen scientists collect data that helps scientists to inventory species and build understanding of relationships to habitat. The data are useful in tracking change over time in species diversity or density, and in investigating impacts of environmental variables such as acid precipitation. You might share with your students the following article about the role of students in rediscovering a springtail species in North Carolina (www.nps.gov/grsm/naturescience/upload/AHSJ%20 Newsletter%202_reduced.pdf, page 3). See Chapter 1, "What Is Citizen Science?" for more information.

Explain

Explore the Terrestrial Invertebrate citizen science dataset to address questions of your choice. You can use data submitted by others or your own data if you have submitted it.

For example, under "Reports, Graphs and Maps," select "Comparing Order Difference by Date." You should see a blank graph and several menu items and notes. You could compare the relative abundance of various orders of invertebrates found in a single sample, or results for up to four samples collected at a single site. For example, in the Site menu, select "Purchase Knob" and "Change Site." (Wait for a new screen to appear.) To compare data from four recent samples, choose this information:

- Primary Data: 08/31/2012 North Windy Ridge
- Comparison 1: 09/07/2012 North Windy Ridge
- Comparison 2: 09/06/2012 North Windy Ridge
- Comparison 3: 09/05/2012 North Windy Ridge

Click the "Graph" button, wait for a graph to appear, and then right-click (control-click on MAC) on the graph and select "Zoom In." Left-click and hold the graph to move it around in the window (Click and hold on MAC). Locate the graph so that you can easily compare results for gastropods (snails/slugs) and coleopterans (beetles).

Model how to ask questions and use the data to answer them.

Sample Question #1: "Did they find more gastropods or more coleopterans in their samples?"

According to the graph, one sample contained coleopterans but not gastropods, one contained gastropods but not coleopterans, one contained both, and the final one contained neither. Totaled across all four samples, they found four gastropods and eight coleopterans. What might this mean, or what might explain this? Perhaps coleopterans are more abundant. By looking at the results for a broader range of samples, we could see if this finding holds across more sites.

Sample Question #2: "Were gastropods more common in some samples than others?"

According to the graph, gastropods were observed in only two of the four samples. In each of the other two samples, two gastropods were observed. What might this mean, or what might explain this result? Two versus zero might just mean that gastropods are generally rare. By looking at the results for other dates, we could see if many were ever found. And by looking at the results for other sites, we could see if gastropods were common in other locations.

Elaborate

After going through examples such as those above, ask students to work in pairs to pose questions of their own and query the citizen science database to seek answers. Some possibilities include:

- Are more insects found in the spring than the summer?

- Are more insects found at lower elevations than higher ones?

- Are different species found at lower elevations than at higher ones?

- Does the number of individuals within a certain taxonomic group differ over the course of a year? If yes, research that particular insect to try to determine why this happens.

Using the website, students can create graphs and charts to analyze questions such as these, or to compare invertebrates found with environmental variables such as temperature and pH.

Evaluate

Pose a question of your own design for students to answer using the Terrestrial Invertebrates database. Ask students to explain the importance of diverse forms of life living in soil and to describe the interdependence of animals in the leaf litter system. Collect and grade their responses.

Extend

Ask each student to select a terrestrial invertebrate and look into its life history, special adaptations, food web importance, and other unique features. As a class, use this information to collectively discuss what roles invertebrates play in food webs and how they contribute to ecosystem functioning.

Lesson Resource

- Terrestrial Invertebrate Data Sheet

References

Nichols, B. 2013. Great Smoky Mountains National Park all taxa biodiversity inventory report. Discover Life in America. *www.dlia.org*

Sachs, S., J. Absher, and A. Carmody. 2011. Instructor's guide to the terrestrial invertebrates website. U.S. Department of the Interior, National Park Service, Appalachian Highlands Science Learning Center in Great Smoky Mountains National Park. *www. handsontheland.org/monitoring/projects/inverts/terr_invert_teach_guide.pdf*

Terrestrial Invertebrate Data Sheet*

Date:	Location:		Collector(s):	
Temp:	Cloud Cover: clear scattered broken overcast	Wind (mph):		Aspect:

3 Dominant Tree Species: 1.   2.   3.

Canopy Cover   0–20%   20–40%   40–60%   60–80%   80–100%

Precipitation (circle one):   Precipitation since last: Date last recorded precip.:
Light Rain / Heavy Rain / Snow / Mist / Sleet

Collecting Method (circle one):
Pit Fall Traps / Flight Intercept Traps / Lundgren Funnel / Beating Sheets / Sweep Nets / Leaf Litter Sifters

Snails (Gastropoda)	Bristletails (Thysanura)	Lacewings (Neuroptera)
Earth Worms (Oligochaeta)	Mayflies (Ephemeroptera)	Adult Beetles (Coleoptera)
Spiders (Araneae)	Grasshoppers etc. (Orthoptera)	Beetle larvae (Coleoptera)
Daddy-long-legs (Opiliones)	Woodroaches (Blattodea)	Caddisflies (Trichoptera)
Mites & Ticks (Acari)	Earwigs (Dermaptera)	Butterflies & Moths (Lepidoptera)
Pseudoscorpiones	Stoneflies (Plecoptera)	Caterpillars (Lepidoptera)
Pill Bugs/Rolly-Pollies (Isopoda)	Booklice/Barklice (Psocoptera)	Adult Flies & Gnats (Diptera)
Millipedes (Diplopoda)	Thrips (Thysanoptera)	Fly and Gnat larvae (Diptera)
Centipedes (Chilopoda)	True Bugs (Hemiptera)	Bees/Ants/Wasps (Hymenoptera)
Springtails (Collembola)	Leafhoppers/Aphids/Cicadas (Homoptera)	Other Unidentified Invertebrates:

Notes:

From the Hands on the Land Terrestrial Invertebrate Monitoring Study

L E S S O N 4

Signs of Spring
Earthworm Inquiry

by Jill Nugent, Texas Tech University

> *"...the return of the humble earthworm, the completion of its vertical migration, is a symbol of the arriving spring."*
>
> **—Edwin Way Teale, North with the Spring (1951)**

Overview

Students brainstorm signs of spring and explore one organism that provides an annual sign of spring's impending arrival—the earthworm!

Learning Objectives

Students will be able to:

- Describe earthworm habitat preferences, life cycles, and behaviors

- Generate and test hypotheses about an organism's habitat preferences

- Collect and interpret data and draw conclusions

Big Idea

In response to seasonal changes, earthworms tunnel deeper into the soil in winter and back to the surface in spring.

Citizen Science Connection

Journey North: A global study of wildlife migration and seasonal change (*www.learner. org/jnorth/season*)

Time Required/Location

Four 30 min. sessions, three indoors and one outdoors

Resources Needed

- Computer with internet access

- Earthworms (often called "night crawlers") 1 per 4 students

- Terrarium habitat

- Clear cup and spoon (1 per group of 4 students)

- Behavior choice trays (1 per group of 4, any type of sturdy containers such as foam trays or shoe boxes will work)

- Black construction paper (1 sheet per group)

- Water

- Sticky notes

- Data sheets (see the end of this lesson for a sample)

- Clipboards

- Soil thermometers (optional)

Background Information

In the fall earthworms migrate downward into the earth to get below the frost line. Hundreds may bunch together and ball up to reduce moisture loss. As the soil warms in the spring, the earthworms begin to migrate again, tunneling upward. This "vertical migration" can be used as a sign of spring. When earthworms appear at the ground surface, they leave the first castings of the new season. Your students may also notice that this is also about the time that the American robin migrates from the South!

Conducting the Activity

Engage

1. As a "warm-up" for the activity, generate discussion by posing questions such as these:

   - How do you know when it's spring? (Students might answer with calendar, sports team activity, or other human-based markers.)

   - What usually happens in nature here (in our local area) when spring is on its way, and when spring finally arrives?

- How might this be different in other parts of the country? Would students in _____ (insert another location here) see different signs of spring than we see? Why or Why not?

2. Have students draw a K-W-Q-L chart in their notebooks and start by filling in what you know (K) about earthworms and what you want to learn (W) about them. Later they will fill out the Q (questions) and L (learned) sections.

Know	Want to Learn	Questions	Learned

3. Introduce students to the Journey North's citizen science project on earthworms (*www.learner.org/jnorth/worm*). Use the data visualization map to pique student interest (*http://www.learner.org/jnorth/worm/index.html*). Ask, "What is citizen science?"

Citizen science refers to efforts in which volunteers partner with professional scientists to collect or analyze data. Citizen scientists in the earthworm study are amassing information from a larger geographic area than any scientist could cover alone, making it possible to explore a variety of inquiry questions (See Frequently Asked Questions at the website). See Chapter 1, "What Is Citizen Science?" for more information.

Explore

Tell students that today they will explore one local sign of spring's arrival—the earthworm! Divide students into groups of four. Have one student from each group use a plastic spoon and clear cup to collect one earthworm from the terrarium. The clear cup will serve as their observation chamber for the worm. Have students observe their worm and address the following in their science notebooks:

- Sketch the organism. Indicate the head/anterior region as well as the tail/posterior end. What evidence indicates which end is which?

- Record at least three observations you have for your organism.

- Record observations of how the earthworm moves.

- Think what questions you have about the earthworm and its behavior. Record these in the Q column of your KWQL chart. Select one question from your group to write on a sticky note, and give it to the teacher to post in the front of the room.

Explain

After the hands-on earthworm exploration, have the students come back together as a class for a debrief time. This will be a whole-class, mostly teacher-led discussion on earthworm adaptations, life cycle, behavior, migration cycle, and classification.

- Discuss student observations.

- Review introductory information about earthworms.

  The Journey North Earthworm page provides useful background information.

- Begin to address the questions that students submitted on the sticky notes. Do not answer questions about habitat preferences at this point because that will be the focus of student investigations in the next section. However, you could prompt students to brainstorm about habitat preference based on their observations and to develop their own research questions and possible investigation procedures to answer those questions. Have students record their questions and investigation procedures in their science notebooks.

Elaborate

1. Students will conduct two experiments about habitat preference using their earthworm. Introduce these two testable questions (or use others designed by your students), and ask students to make a prediction about each in their science notebooks.

   - Experiment #1: Does the earthworm prefer moist or dry environments?

     Students will set up their behavior choice trays with one side dry and the other moistened with a bit of water. The earthworm will then be placed in the middle and students will watch for 2–3 minutes to see which side it moves to. Students will record their findings in their notebooks, and will also record the data at the front of the room where all class data will be compiled.

- Experiment #2: Does the earthworm prefer dark or light environments?

  Students will prepare their behavior choice trays so that one end is shaded with black construction paper and the other is unshaded. Data will be recorded as above.

2. When all groups have finished collecting and reporting their findings, place the earthworms back in the classroom terrarium. On the blackboard or a large sheet of paper, construct two tables and compile the class data for each inquiry question. Have students copy this compiled data into their notebooks, and instruct them to construct a bar graph of the class findings for each experiment.

3. Talk about graphs and how they are a visual representation of the numbers in the data tables. Begin discussion of the findings, pushing students to connect their explanations with evidence and to explore alternative explanations. Discuss what these findings tell us about earthworm habitat preference—in what types of environment would we expect to find earthworms? Give students an opportunity to summarize their reasoning and explanations in their notebooks.

4. Ask students what other testable questions they can think of related to earthworms?

   For example, they might come up with questions related to temperature or food preferences.

Evaluate

1. Have students complete their K-W-Q-L chart by filling in the final column indicating what they have learned about earthworms.

2. Collect student science notebooks for further evaluation.

Extend

1. Early in the spring, provide students with data sheets (see sample) for recording earthworm sightings and signs (such as castings, a student

favorite and very easy to locate! Castings are the worms' digestive waste products and look like small piles of pilled soil.) Remind students about the environments that earthworms prefer, and take them outside to look for worms. Aim for this first time outside to be a quick check when the ground is likely to be too cold for worms to have emerged.

2. As time permits, continue checking briefly for earthworms in the school yard as the weather warms, and urge students to keep an eye out for them in their yards, parks, or other green spaces. As the ground begins to warm, have students take temperature readings of the soil in places where you think you might see worms and in places where you don't expect to see them. Continue recording temperatures in regular intervals. Try to get a reading at the soil surface and at depths of 3, 6, and 12 inches. Graph data and compare across time and space. Indicate on the graph when earthworms appeared. What do the graphs reveal about the worms' temperature preferences or requirements?

3. Once earthworms have been sighted, have students submit the date to Journey North and use the "View Sightings" feature to compare their date with others around the country.

4. Have the class (or groups of students) pick another species from Journey North to monitor and report phenology data/observations over a certain interval of time. Examples include: barn swallows, frogs, monarch butterflies, hummingbirds, tulips, robins, and more! The class could pick a species to monitor and enter sightings each week into the Journey North website, or simply follow sightings that have been entered by others to track migrations and seasonal changes.

Lesson Resource

- Sample Data Sheet

Sample Data Sheet

Observers _____

Date _____ Start Time of Day _____ End Time of Day _____

Outdoor Temperature _____ Wind Speed & Direction _____

% Cloud Cover _____ Number of days since last rain/snow event _____

Latitude and Longitude of Survey Site _____

Sketch of Survey Area

Indicate on this sketch where earthworms were observed and how many. Also indicate the locations of any earthworm castings.

Animated Maps for Animated Discussions

by Jennifer Fee, Cornell Lab of Ornithology

Overview

Students use critical-thinking skills to draw conclusions from animated maps portraying bird population dynamics throughout the year, and they consider the role of modeling in scientific research and environmental conservation.

Learning Objectives

Students will be able to:

- Compare and contrast animated maps portraying seasonal changes in distribution of a migratory and non-migratory species of bird

- Identify "food preference" as a key indicator of whether a bird species will migrate or remain in one area year-round

- Relate migration to habitat requirements and explain how these differ between species

- Describe the role of modeling in understanding data and making scientific predictions

Resources Needed

- Computer with internet access

- Interactive whiteboard or projector

Big Idea

Some birds migrate during breeding season to areas with richer food supplies, and food preferences are a key indicator in predicting which species are migratory. Animated maps produced with eBird citizen science data are useful in analyzing annual migration patterns of bird species.

Citizen Science Connection

eBird (*http://ebird.org*)

Time Required/Location

60–90 minutes, indoors

Background Information

eBird is a citizen science project in which anyone can report birds they have seen. The resulting database contains many millions of observations. Scientists are creating models that combine these bird sightings with data on factors such as habitat, climate, human population density, and demographics. The models run on supercomputers to churn through huge amounts of data and come up with predictions of bird population distribution over time. Modeling makes it possible to predict bird occurrence even in places and times for which data are lacking and to create animated maps that portray week-to-week variations in the likelihood of seeing each species in a given location from week to week throughout the year. For migratory species, the maps vividly illustrate the timing and location of seasonal movements between nesting and wintering grounds. Ecologists have begun using this information to identify, prioritize, and coordinate conservation actions targeted to protect species though all stages of their annual cycles.

See Chapter 4 ("Case Study: Connecting With Students Through Birds") for further information and stories about teachers integrating eBird and animated maps into their science teaching.

Conducting the Activity

Engage

1. Show the students this "mystery" animated map (*http://ebird.org/results/STEM/ animations/NOCA_large.gif*). Ask them what they think the map might be showing. Note all answers at this time and don't yet give hints or provide correct answers.

2. Show a second animated map (*http://ebird.org/content/ebird/news/patterns-from-ebird-eastern-phoebe*). Again, ask students what they think the map might be showing.

3. Explain that the maps portray expected occurrence of two species of birds throughout a year. They were created using a computer model that combines citizen science bird observation data with about 60 environmental variables.

4. Initiate a compare-and-contrast discussion of these two maps by drawing a Venn diagram such as the one below.

5. Reveal the type of data portrayed on these maps: the distribution of a non-migratory bird (northern cardinal) over the course of a year, and the same for a migratory species (eastern phoebe). Discuss, and add to or correct the Venn diagram.

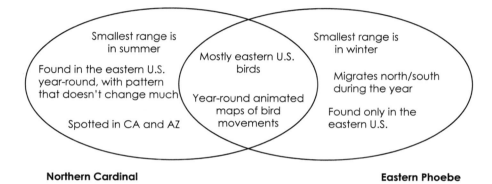

Northern Cardinal

Eastern Phoebe

As you can see in Figure 5.1 (p. 96), the distribution of northern cardinals remains relatively constant throughout the year, compared with eastern phoebes that migrate northward in spring and back south in the fall.

6. If desired, discuss the aim of this sort of modeling, for example asking why scientists would bother to create these complicated models when plenty of data are available showing where each species has been seen at various times throughout the year.

Modeling makes it possible to predict bird distribution patterns for times and places where data are not available—such as into the future, or in relatively inaccessible locations where birding is difficult or impossible. Students might wonder why the cardinal map shows a bit of seasonal variation even though this species does not migrate. The primary reason is because it is harder to detect cardinals at certain times of year, and they are less likely to be reported to eBird by citizen scientists at those times. In the spring, colorful male cardinals sing frequently to defend their territories and attract mates. During the summer, they become more secretive while raising their young. In early September cardinals tend to hide because they are molting and vulnerable to predators. In

FIGURE 5.1.

Snapshots from animated eBird maps showing northern cardinal and eastern phoebe occurrence in 2008

The brightest areas indicate the greatest likelihood of seeing each species if you were bird watching at that particular time of year.

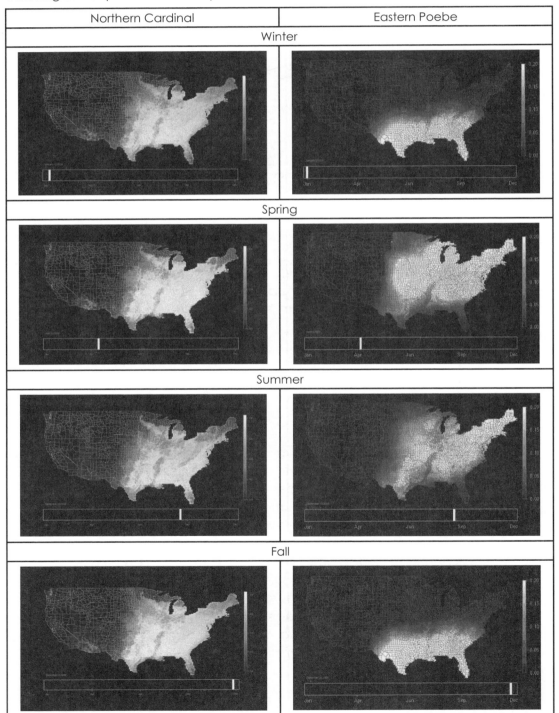

winter, however, cardinals become a familiar sight because they gather in flocks at bird feeders and other food-rich areas.

Explore

Ask a series of questions to assess student understanding:

- What is migration?

When scientists speak of migration, they are usually referring to seasonal migration, or the large-scale annual movement of all or part of a population between its breeding (summer) and nonbreeding (wintering) grounds. Migration is a cycle that birds repeat each year in response to the change of seasons, almost always based on the availability of food.

- What is citizen science?

Citizen science *refers to efforts in which volunteers partner with professional scientists to collect or analyze data about the natural world. Through the Cornell Lab's citizen science projects, people around the world follow protocols to collect data about their local birds and contribute these observations to databases that are used by researchers, students, and the public to better understand bird distribution, abundance, and population trends. See Chapter 1, "What Is Citizen Science?" for more information.*

- What information can we derive from these maps?

Examples include: where each species is found, what habitats it prefers, whether it changes in distribution over the course of a year, and how it compares with other species in terms of distribution and habitat preferences

- What factors other than migration might influence whether people see birds within a selected area over various times of year?

Birds are more visible during the spring because during breeding season they call attention to themselves with bright colors and songs. Once nesting begins, they tend to be quieter and more hidden to protect their young from predators. For species such as cardinals that do not migrate, the map still shows some seasonal changes. These fluctuations are likely due to changes in detectability, with fewer people reporting seeing the bird when it is sitting quietly on its nest rather than singing and displaying to attract a mate and defend the territory.

Explain

Show photos of the northern cardinal and eastern phoebe, from All About Birds or another source. Ask students to brainstorm reasons why they think that these birds, which are similar in size and have some overlapping habitat needs, are different in the fact that one migrates long distances and the other does not.

Birds need to eat a lot to keep going, and they need even more food when they are feeding their nestlings. Access to food is critical during migration and when birds are raising young. The need to feed and raise nestlings is the main reason many birds don't just stay in the warm tropics all year round. Although the tropics have a good climate, there is also a lot of competition for food. Going north in the summer offers migrating birds a huge explosion of food sources, such as insects. Some birds, such as phoebes, eat insects year round, and others, such as the cardinal, have seed-eating beaks and can survive by eating seeds during the winter.

Elaborate

Research migratory and nonmigratory birds to investigate the role of food preference in determining which species migrate.

Evaluate Show students another animated map and ask them to draw conclusions about the species. For example, try the Wood Thrush (*http://ebird.org/content/ebird/about/occurrence-maps/wood-thrush*) for an eastern bird, or the western tanager (*http://ebird.org/content/ebird/about/occurrence-maps/western-tanager*) for a western one. For a bird that is found across the United States but shows a different migration pattern, try the American pipit, a species that breeds in the Rocky Mountains and the arctic (*http://ebird.org/content/ebird/about/occurrence-maps/american-pipit*).

For each species, ask:

- What is this species' range?

- How does this map compare with ones for previously viewed species? Does this species appear to be migratory? How can you tell?

- What do you think the bird eats?

- Can you tell anything about habitat preferences of this species? (For example, does it appear to breed along coastlines, or in areas where you know there are rivers or mountain ranges? Check the midsummer maps to explore this type of question).

Extend

1. With so much data available on where birds have actually been seen, why bother with modeling? Discuss what additional information the models can provide.

   One reason for modeling is to fill in the gaps where no data are available. Although eBird has an impressive and ever-growing database, the data primarily represent areas where people are most likely to go birding, and there are regions for which little or no data have been submitted. The models also can be used to predict population dynamics into the future, and to look at expected responses to various changes in environmental conditions. The model outputs are revealing new information about relationships between birds and their environment and about the annual cycles of North American birds.

2. Assign small groups of students to select one species' occurrence map (*http://ebird.org/content/ebird/about/occurrence-maps/occurrence-maps*) and explain, how this bird differs from the ones the entire class has viewed. Questions might include:

   - Does your bird seem to show a migratory pattern? If so, what is it?

   - What questions does the animated map raise for you in terms of this bird's behavior over the course of a year?

   Have students investigate a question of their choice by reading about their species and reporting their findings to the class.

3. Invite students to participate in eBird by identifying and counting local birds. The Cornell Lab of Ornithology's *BirdSleuth: Most Wanted Birds* curriculum makes it easy to identify birds and contribute data to eBird. Find more information at *www.birdsleuth.org*.

On the Web

- All About Birds (*www.allaboutbirds.org*): Photos and information about behavior and habitat preferences of bird species featured in eBird animated maps.

- eBird animated maps (*http://ebird.org/content/ebird/about/occurrence-maps*): Overview of the models used to produce eBird's animated occurrence maps and links to the maps and related information about migration and behavior of each species portrayed

Additional Resources

Marris, E. 2010. Birds flock online. *Nature News. www.nature.com/news/2010/100810/full/ news.2010.395.html*
Summary: A news-style overview of eBird and the animated maps

Wood, C., B. Sullivan, M. Iliff, D. Fink, and S. Kelling. 2011. eBird: Engaging birders in science and conservation. *PLoS Biology* 9 (12): e1001220. *www.plosbiology.org/article/ info%3Adoi%2F10.1371%2Fjournal.pbio.1001220*
Summary: An in-depth explanation of eBird and the models that produce the animated maps

L E S S O N 6

Bird Migration Patterns in My Area*

by Jennifer Fee, Cornell Lab of Ornithology

Overview

Students consider indicators of climate change, interpret various representations of eBird citizen science data, and reflect on how their actions as citizen scientists can assist in better understanding bird migration as a local indicator of climate change.

Learning Objectives

Students will be able to:

- Define *migration* and relate it to habitat preferences of individual bird species

- Use citizen science data outputs to interpret trends in bird migration occurrence and timing

- Name at least two factors that impact changes in animal populations over time

Big Idea

Trends in citizen science data collected over time can indicate the influence of changes in habitat, including those caused by climate change.

Citizen Science Connection

eBird (*http://ebird.org*)

Time Required/Location

90–120 minutes, indoors

* Modified from Bird Migration: A Local Indicator of Climate Change, by Julia Skolnik and Jessica Jones, The Franklin Institute

Resources Needed

- Computers with internet access

- Projector and screen

- Speakers

- Handout

- Additional resources on bird migration patterns (optional)

Background Information

Although migrating birds use photoperiod (length of daylight) as their major guide during migration, they will use local favorable weather conditions to their advantage as well. eBird is a citizen science project in which anyone, anywhere in the world, can submit their bird sightings online. The massive database housing these results is proving valuable to scientists conducting research on a variety of topics including adaptations of bird species to changes in climate or other aspects of the environment. A recent study using eBird data found that many migratory species, including the red-eyed vireo and scarlet tanager, tend to arrive at their nesting grounds earlier in warm years and later in cold years. However, other species such as the barn swallow and eastern wood-pewee do not seem to be adapting in this way to climate variation, and their populations may be suffering as a result (Hurlbert and Liang 2012).

See Chapter 4, "Case Study: Connecting With Students Through Birds," for further information and stories about teachers integrating eBird and animated maps into their science teaching.

Conducting the Activity

Engage

1. Ask students about the birds they have observed in their yards, at school, or at a local park:

   a. What kinds of birds have you seen? If you don't know the names, what do they look like?

   b. Which species do you notice year-round? Are there others that you see only in the summer or only in some other season? What is migration?

c. Where do you typically see birds?

d. Are the birds you see usually alone or in groups? What are they doing?

2. Watch video about changes in timing of bird behavior at *www.fi.edu/birds* (Bird Behavior). Engage students in a discussion about observed changes in bird behavior.

a. Ask: What evidence of changes in migration timing were noted in the video? What is changing about birds' behavior patterns? What have scientists noticed? What did the scientists say this could mean?

b. Why do you think this is happening? Do you think it is a problem? Why or why not?

In a warmer than usual spring, insects emerge and plants bloom earlier than usual. Migratory birds may not arrive in time to sync with these food sources because they cannot perceive and respond to cues when they are in their wintering ground hundreds or perhaps even thousands of miles away.

3. Ask students, "What is citizen science?"

Citizen science *refers to efforts in which volunteers partner with professional scientists to collect or analyze data. In the eBird citizen science project, any person anywhere in the world can submit information about the birds they have observed. This is creating a massive database with over one million new bird observations entered each month! The data are useful for exploring bird population dynamics and relationships to habitat. For example, we will use eBird data to find out what bird species live in our area, and which of them migrate. The data also are useful in tracking responses to global climate change such as changes in location of individual species or the timing of their migratory flights. See Chapter 1, "What Is Citizen Science?" for more information.*

Explore

1. Using eBird's "Explore Data" function, select "Bar Charts" and select your state or other region of interest. Figure 6.1 shows an example chart for New York State. Take a look at the bar charts for your area. Do you see any species with thick green bars stretching across the entire year? (These species

FIGURE 6.1.

Bar chart showing monthly occurrence of bird species in New York State

(Only a portion of the full list is shown here.)

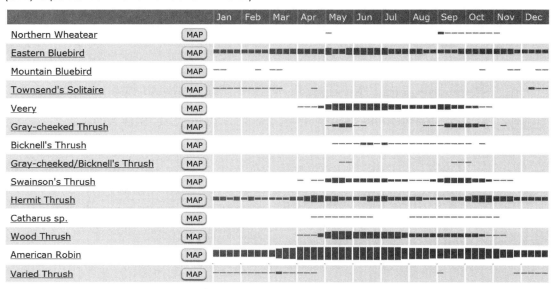

are present year-round.) And other species for which the green bars get much shorter or disappear entirely in certain seasons? (These species are migratory.) Looking at the bar chart for your area, what are some species that remain year-round? Are there others that migrate to your area for the summer breeding season? Are others present only in winter months, or pass through and are seen only during the spring and fall migratory periods?

In Figure 6.1, for example, you can see that eastern bluebirds and American robins are seen in New York year-round, whereas veeries and wood thrushes are seen there only in summer months. The gray-cheeked thrush migrates through New York in spring and fall, but isn't present in summer or winter.

2. Using eBird's "Line Graphs" function, create a graph comparing frequency of sightings of two bird species—one that is migratory and another that is resident year-round. For example, in Figure 6.2 you can see that yellow warbler sightings drop almost to zero in winter months in New York, whereas northern cardinals are commonly seen year-round.

FIGURE 6.2.

Frequency of sighting of northern cardinals and yellow warblers in New York State

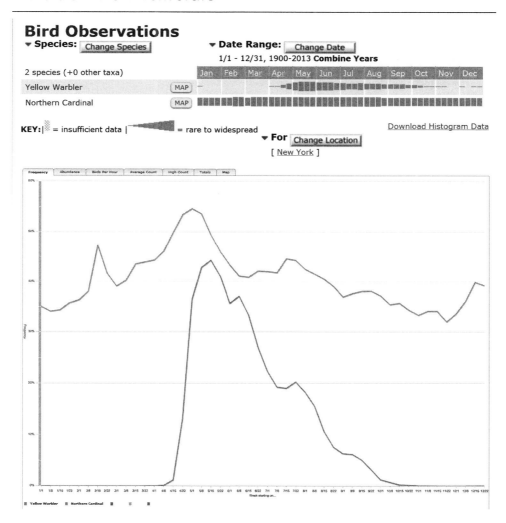

3. Discuss the meaning of *frequency* as used in these graphs.

In eBird, "Frequency" refers to the percentage of birding check-lists within a defined region and range of dates that include that particular species. A simpler way to think about this is that it represents the chance you would see this species if you were to go birding in that region at that time of year.

4. Ask students why they think one species stays through the winter and another migrates to a different wintering ground?

   In this case, the yellow warbler eats insects, which are not present in New York in the winter. In contrast, the northern cardinal eats seeds that are available all winter long. The beaks of these two species are quite different and adapted for eating these specific types of foods.

Explain

As a group, investigate whether migratory species in your area have changed their migratory habits over the years.

1. List up to five species that are found in your area only during the summer. These are migratory species that breed in your state. For example, using Figure 6.1, the Veery and Wood Thrush would be excellent choices.

2. Again navigate to the "Explore Data" tab and click on the "Line Graph" option. Select up to five species of interest that migrate. Set Location to your state and Date Range to "1900–1965." Grab a screen capture of the resultant graph (see Figure 6.3 as an example, p. 108). Then run again with the date set to "2010" ending with the current date (see Figure 6.4, p. 109). Again grab a screen capture so you will be able to compare to the historic query.

Note differences in the two graphs (and look up explanations if possible). In this example, it is evident that the turkey vulture overwinters in New York in recent years, but didn't arrive until March in the historic query. What are some explanations?

   Climate change is one possible explanation. However, other habitat changes also could be responsible. For example, a student could suggest that more automobile traffic is leading to more road kill. More dead animals means more food for scavenging turkey vultures, an explanation that has nothing to do with climate change. Also note that the differences in sample size could also account for some differences—with more checklists entered in recent years, there is a greater chance that someone will detect a species.

The wood Thrush arrives around the same date historically and today (around April 15), but it is reported less frequently today than in the past. What are some explanations?

According to the All About Birds website, wood thrush is a forest species that has declined 43% since 1966, with threats to both its North American breeding grounds and Central American wintering grounds. Forest fragmentation in North American forests has resulted in both increased nest predation and increased cowbird parasitism, significantly reducing their reproductive success. Another factor is acid precipitation. A study by the Cornell Laboratory of Ornithology was the first large-scale analysis that linked acid rain to this thrush's decline, attributed to loss of carbon needed to create the birds' eggs. For further information, see Chu and Hames (2002).

Elaborate

1. Invite students to think about migratory birds they know in their area. Ask: "What birds live here, and when do they come and go?" Have students select a migratory species of interest. Using sources such as the All About Birds website, the "Range and Point Maps" feature in eBird, or a printed field guide, ask students to identify the summer (breeding) and winter (non-breeding) regions for their species. Where do birds of that species go when not in your region?

2. Draw students' attention to bird migration patterns as a possible local indicator of climate change. Highlight the parts of the video (shown in the Engage portion of this lesson) that noted bird migration patterns. Ask students why they think studying bird migration can help us understand more about changes in our global climate. Summarize other possible explanations for changes in arrival and departure dates and frequency of sightings.

Evaluate

1. Encourage students to work in pairs or groups with the eBird database and the "Bird Migration in My Area: eBird Data Collection Table" to determine the recent arrival and departure dates of five species of migratory birds in your county or state and to organize these species according to the timing of their migratory flights. Tell them to be prepared to share these trends with the class.

FIGURE 6.3.

Frequency of sightings of four migratory species in New York State, 1900–1965

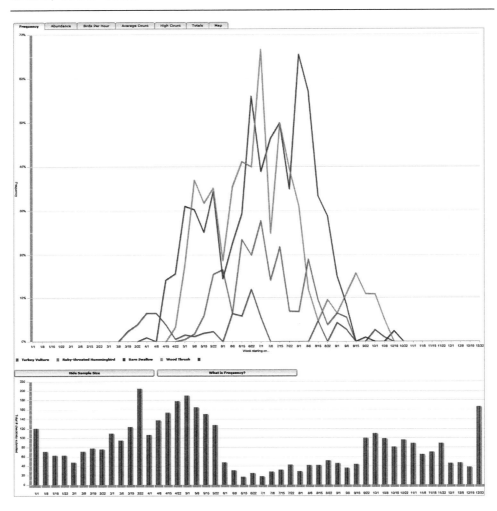

FIGURE 6.4.

Frequency of sightings of the same four species in New York State, 2010 to present

Note the difference in scales between Figures 3 and 4 (In the frequency graph, the historic scale ranges up to 70%, whereas the modern scale is only 40%; the sample size scale is only 160 historically but goes up to 7,000 sightings in the modern graph).

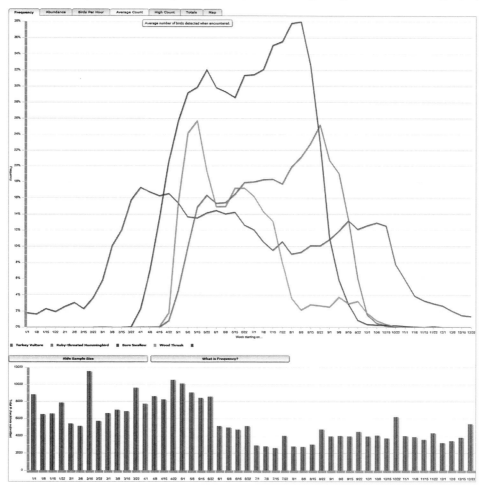

- Ask students to describe at least two factors that might impact changes in animal populations over time.

- After students have documented trends, encourage them to share preliminary findings they have made based on the eBird database.

- Note if any students found conflicting trends, and encourage them to use sufficient evidence to support their explanations.

Extend

Consider implementing additional lessons from the Franklin Institute's Communicating Climate Change curriculum (Skolnik and Jones 2011). One option is to take students outside to observe birds. You could invite a local bird expert to accompany your class on a field trip to a local birding hotspot. After registering your class with an eBird account, your students can record bird sightings and submit a collated class list to eBird. For a longer-term study, they could go birding once a week (or other interval of your choice), and submit each collated class list to eBird. The Cornell Lab of Ornithology offers a curriculum kit that supports learning about bird diversity and identification and supports teachers and students participating in eBird and querying the eBird database (Fee, Rosenberg, DeRado, and Trautmann 2011).

Lesson Resource

- Bird Migration in My Area: eBird Data Collection Table

On the Web

- All About Birds (*www.allaboutbirds.org*): Photos and information about behavior, habitat preferences, and range maps of bird species

- eBird (*http://ebird.org*): A citizen science project that collects and displays data about birds from around the world

- NASA, Global Climate Change (*http://climate.nasa.gov*): A website that documents the evidence, causes, and effects of climate change

References

Chu, M., and S. Hames. 2002. Wood thrush declines linked to acid rain: Citizen scientists collected key data. *BirdScope* 16 (4): Autumn. *www.birds.cornell.edu/Publications/ Birdscope/ Autumn2002/wood_thrush.html*

Fee, J. M., A. Rosenberg, L. DeRado, and N. M. Trautmann. 2011. *BirdSleuth most wanted birds, Version 2.* Ithaca, NY: Cornell Lab of Ornithology.

Hurlbert A. H., and Z. Liang. 2012. Spatiotemporal variation in avian migration phenology: Citizen science reveals effects of climate change. *PLoS ONE* 7 (2): e31662. *www. plosone.org/article/ info%3Adoi%2F10.1371%2Fjournal.pone.0031662*

Skolnik, J., and J. Jones. 2011. *Bird migration: A local indicator of climate change.* Philadelphia, PA: The Franklin Institute.

Additional Resources

Walther, G., E. Post, P. Convey, A. Menzel, C. Pamresan, T. J. C. Beebee, J. Fromentin, O. Hoegh-Guldberg, and F. Bairlein. 2002. Ecological responses to recent climate change. *Nature* (416): 389–395. *www.nature.com/nature/journal/v416/n6879/full/416389a.html*
Summary: A scientific article about evidence of the ecological impacts of recent climate change on flora and fauna from polar to tropical environments

Wood, C., B. Sullivan, M. Iliff, D. Fink, and S. Kelling. 2011. eBird: Engaging birders in science and conservation. *PLoS Biology* 9 (12): e1001220. *www.plosbiology.org/article/ info%3Adoi%2F10.1371%2Fjournal.pbio.1001220*
Summary: In-depth explanation of eBird and scientific models produced with its data

Bird Migration Patterns in My Area
eBird Data Collection Table

Name:_____

Bird Sighting Hotspot: _____   Date Range (years): _____

Bird Species Name	Arrival Week	Departure Week	Notes

Which species arrived the earliest?

Which species arrived the latest?

Which species is present in your area for the shortest time?

L E S S O N 7

Habitat Matters

YardMap Your School Yard

by Nancy M. Trautmann, Jennifer Fee, and Jennifer Goforth, Cornell Lab of Ornithology

Overview

Through mapping and planning habitat improvements in their school yard or other open area, students learn about the importance of small-scale habitat management and discover the characteristics of green spaces that create productive habitat for birds.

Learning Objectives

Students will be able to:

- Define key elements of habitat in support of a diverse range of bird species and other wildlife

- Analyze a green space to determine its potential for providing food, water, and shelter

- Plan and carry out conservation measures to make a green space more bird friendly

- Contribute data to the YardMap citizen science protocol

Big Idea

Habitat elements include food, water, cover, and space. By improving or providing these elements, people can help birds in their yards, school yards, and other spaces.

Citizen Science Connection

YardMap (*www.yardmap.org*)

Time Required/Location

Two 60-minute class periods, indoors and outdoors

Resources Needed

- Computers with internet access

- Interactive whiteboard or projector

- Notebooks in which to take bird and plant notes

- Printouts of an aerial view of your school yard, created by taking a screen shot of your site on the YardMap website (1 per student) (If this is too dark to provide a good base map for annotation by students, a simple map of the school yard can be used instead.)

- Clipboards

- One camera for each group, along with the necessary equipment to upload pictures to a computer (optional)

- Selection of native plants or other materials selected for habitat improvement, and associated gardening tools (optional)

Background Information

Growth in the amount of lawns across the United States is not good news for birds. How we manage and maintain our lawns, school yards, and other open spaces makes a big difference to birds because the typical manicured lawn provides little in the way of food, water, and shelter needed for a productive bird habitat. Lawns tend to consist of only one or two species of grass, dramatically limiting the potential wildlife they can support. You may think that birds eat only seeds, but in fact they also eat insects, fruits, berries, nuts, nectar, and other animals. Adding some native vegetation provides nutritious seeds, fruits, berries, and even insects that wouldn't otherwise be available. Greater diversity of vegetation supports a greater diversity of foods (especially insects) that birds can eat and feed to their young, resulting in more diverse and abundant bird life. The YardMap Network provides a place to map the habitat characteristics of your school yard, learn about ways to make this space more bird-friendly, track conservation-related improvements on your map, and share with an online community of people interested in establishing safe and productive habitats for birds (Figure 7.1).

Conducting the Activity

Before digging in, set up a YardMap account. You may wish to create a centralized user account with an independent e-mail address, username, and password

FIGURE 7.1.

An example site mapped in YardMap

Source: yardmap.org

to share with your students. For more information, see "Tips for Groups Using YardMap" under the "Help" function.

Engage

1. Ask students to imagine that they are a bird—any bird. Ask: What are you doing? Where do you live? What do you see? Now focus more on habitat needs. What do you eat? Where do you find food? How do you eat? Where do you find water? Where do you sleep? Where do you lay your eggs? Where would you hide if something scared you? After plenty of imagination time, ask students to share ideas as a group, pair up and interview a partner about his or her story, draw the adventure, or write a creative story about the life of an individual bird.

2. As a group, brainstorm a list of ideas about what birds need for survival. Write ideas on the board, grouping them into categories representing food, water, cover, and space. If things in all four categories have not been mentioned, continue the discussion and encourage deeper thinking. If other things, such as "love" or "parents" are mentioned, put them in a separate place on the board for non-habitat needs. Once the list is complete, summarize that all living things need a place that supplies their own specific needs with regard to types of food, water, cover, and space. Together these make

up that organism's habitat. If an animal, such as a bird, cannot find these things in an area, and in the right arrangement, its habitat needs are not met and it will not be able to survive there.

FIGURE 7.2.

An example chart showing the four categories of needs related to habitat

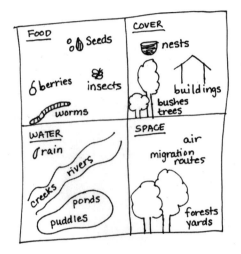

Explore

1. Tell students that they are going to create a detailed map of their school yard, paying special attention to ways in which it helps to meet habitat needs of birds and other wildlife, and they will submit this map to a citizen science project called YardMap. Find your school yard in YardMap and project the aerial image. With guidance from the class, ask one student to use YardMap's tools to outline the boundaries of your space. Have the rest of the class draw a similar outline on their printouts of the aerial view of the school yard.

2. Ask students, "What is citizen science, and how does it relate to YardMap?"

   Citizen science refers to efforts in which volunteers partner with professional scientists to collect or analyze data. The YardMap Network is a citizen science project designed to inspire people to create better habitat for birds in their yards, school yards, and other open spaces. In YardMap, people map the characteristics of these green spaces, learn about potential ways to improve bird habitat, and track changes they have made in the landscape. Networking with other participants provides opportunities to share conservation strategies, challenges, and successes. Scientists are using the data represented in everyone's maps to investigate questions such as what practices best improve the wildlife value of residential landscapes and over how large an area must they

*be implemented in order to make a difference. See Chapter 1,
"What Is Citizen Science?" for more information.*

3.   Break into small groups to go outside and collect data about the space
     you have outlined. If possible, provide each group with a camera, and tell
     students to bring their aerial view printout and a pen or pencil for making
     annotations. Assign tasks using one of two options:

     •   If the area you wish to map is large, or students are accustomed
         to independent work, consider having each group map and
         photographically document a separate piece of the total space.

     •   If the area is small or students require more supervision, have each
         group map and photograph selected aspects of the overall habitat (for
         example, Group 1 maps the trees, Group 2 the shrubs, and so on).

4.   Instruct students to investigate their assigned area with the goal of refining
     the map. They should look for different kinds of land cover and sketch the
     boundaries of areas covered by pavement, buildings, lawn, grasses, flow-
     ers/herbs, forest, shrubs, water, wetlands, and bare ground (dirt, gravel, or
     sand). Then they should think about where birds might find food, water,
     and cover and add information to their maps to indicate bird-friendly plants
     or objects such as bird feeders, water sources, and brushy areas.

Explain

Back in the classroom, discuss what the students found outside. In YardMap, use the
"Tool Shed" to refine your map, for example by creating polygons indicating areas
covered by lawn, garden, or shrubs and adding features such as individual trees, bird
feeders, or a rock pile. View photos taken by students. If you wish to include photos
on your YardMap site, you will first need to upload them to a site you can link to
(such as Flickr or your school's website). When you place an object icon on your map,
you can click on it, select "open" and then provide information and links to photos.

Elaborate

1.   Ask students to create a chart similar to Figure 7.2 but including only items
     found in their study site, using their data as evidence in constructing expla-
     nations for which parts of the school yard provide the most basic habitat
     necessities for birds. If the school yard does not provide food, water, and
     cover, what is lacking?

2. Ask students if they saw any birds while exploring the school yard. If so, what were the birds doing?

3. As homework or in class, ask students to explore the YardMap website and come up with ideas for making the schoolyard more bird friendly and justifying these suggestions with evidence they collected from the site or other sources. Encourage them to use the "Explore" and "Learn" sections of YardMap's site. In the "Explore" section, they can type in your school's ZIP code and bring up information about your local ecoregion, community gardens, native plant species, regional guidance in planting for pollinators, and contact information for local experts for further information and assistance. This section also provides a listing and mapped locations of birds reported to eBird within 20 miles of that ZIP code over the past 30 days. The "Learn" section provides detailed information about all aspects of bird habitat and bird-friendly landscaping.

Evaluate

Assign students to write a one-page essay describing the extent to which the schoolyard currently provides food, water, and shelter for birds and outlining one or more steps they would like to propose for improving it in terms of bird habitat. The Additional Resources section lists references that provide detailed guidance for a variety of habitat improvement efforts.

Example responses might be to hang up bird feeders, plant fruit-bearing trees or shrubs, put in a birdbath, clean up trash, install nest boxes, plant native wildflowers, or even create a wetland.

Extend

Compile a class list of plans outlined by students, and select one or more habitat improvement steps to implement as a class project. If you have the opportunity to carry out this lesson with multiple classes or in multiple years, you could start from scratch with each group or cumulatively build an increasingly detailed map and increasingly bird-friendly habitat. Students could present their habitat improvement plans to the school administration for approval and to parent or community organizations for help with fundraising through efforts such as selling bird houses, native plants, or birdseed.

If students identify birds seen in the schoolyard and submit these data to eBird (*http://ebird.org*), they can also use eBird's online data outputs to follow trends and determine whether changes occur in bird diversity or abundance in conjunction with your habitat improvement efforts.

Additional Resources

Kolstad, C., K. Vollherbst, and K. K. Mullin. 2011. *Schoolyard habitat project guide, 2nd ed*. U.S. Fish & Wildlife Service. *www.fws.gov/cno/pdf/HabitatGuideColor.pdf*
Summary: A how-to guide stepping through planning, installing and sustaining a school yard habitat improvement project including specific considerations for creation or restoration of woodlands, meadows, and wetlands

Kress, S. 2006. *The Audubon Society guide to attracting birds: Creating natural habitats for properties large and small, 2nd ed*. Ithaca, NY: Cornell University Press.
Summary: A guide to attracting birds by planting native species and providing water and nest sites

Tallamy, D. 2009. *Bringing nature home: How you can sustain wildlife with native plants*. Portland, OR: Timber Press.
Summary: Explains the ecological link between native plant species and native wildlife, with insects that feed on native plants playing key roles in the food webs supporting birds and other wildlife.

Zickfoose, J. 2001. *The bird-friendly backyard: Natural gardening for birds: Simple ways to create a bird haven*. Emmaus, PA: Rodale Press.
Summary: A guide to creating plantings that attract, feed, and shelter birds and butterflies

Winter Twig Investigation

*by Patricia Otto, Pacific Education Institute, Olympia, WA, and
Jane Ulrich, Sunny Hills Elementary, Sammamish, WA*

Overview

Students view a twig as a living system. They observe twigs on deciduous trees or shrubs throughout the winter, collect data indicating when the buds burst into leaf or flower, and submit their data to Project BudBurst. Tracking change over time in the appearance of their twigs builds students' skills in observing, recording data, and posing scientific questions based on their observations. They also teach younger students about their tree or shrub.

Learning Objectives

Students will be able to:

- Describe the physical characteristics of a deciduous twig in winter

- Note changes in twigs over time and record first evidence of buds bursting into leaf or flower

- Describe the twig as a system including inputs and outputs along with the factors that determine when buds open

Big Idea

Twigs of deciduous trees and shrubs annually produce buds that contain the beginnings of leaves, stems, and flowers that will emerge and grow.

Citizen Science Connection

Project BudBurst (*www.budburst.org*), with maps at (*www.budburst.fieldscope.org*)

Time Required/Location

Five or six 60-minute sessions, plus time daily to observe trees or shrubs in the spring; indoors and outdoors extensions could use another two or three sessions.

Resources Needed

- Computer with internet access

- Interactive whiteboard or computer projector

- Outdoor area with accessible trees or shrubs

- Twigs that can be cut apart and observed

- Winter twig ID book for your area (optional)

- Measuring tape

- Magnifying glasses

- Data sheet "How Do Twigs Change Over Time?" (1 per student)

- Data sheet "Regular Reports" or "Single Report" from Project BudBurst

- Clipboards

- Students' science notebooks

Background Information

Students learning about life cycles and seasonal change can submit observations to Project BudBurst, a national citizen science project that tracks the timing of biological events such as plant growth and flowering in relation to abiotic factors such as changes in season and climate. In Project BudBurst, citizen scientists record phenological events such as the first leaf, first flower, and first ripe fruit for a variety of plant species, with emphasis on native species. Such data make it possible for scientists and students to detect trends over time and study the responses of individual plant species to climatic variation locally, regionally, and nationally.

Conducting the Activity

Select a site in your school yard or nearby where twigs are accessible on deciduous trees or shrubs. Project Budburst provides guidance in selecting species to observe. Note that accurate species identification is important if you wish to submit data to Project Budburst. Because it can be quite difficult to identify bare trees or shrubs during winter months, it is best to start when leaves, flowers, and/or fruits are present. You therefore may wish to identify the plants in the fall, either on your own or have your students begin their twig studies then so it will be possible for them to identify the species.

Before beginning data collection, visit the Project Budburst site to see where and how data are submitted and to download appropriate data collection sheets for the species your students will be observing. The Classroom Implementation Guide offers useful tips on how to get started. Take a look at the two options for submitting data, and decide which will work better with your schedule. "Regular Reports" require checking the plant a few times each week in the growing season to watch for and record when it reaches various stages of leafing, flowering, and fruiting. If periodic observations are not possible, students can submit one or more "Single Reports" to record individual observations of their study plant. If your students are under the age of 13, an adult will have to work with them to register on the project website (see the Educators pages on the site for more information).

Engage

1. Show a video of flowers bursting into bloom, such as *http://player.vimeo.com/ video/ 27920977?title=0&%3bbyline=0&%3bportrait=0href* and use this as a springboard for discussion about seasonal changes in plants. You could note that deciduous trees and shrubs lose their foliage in winter months whereas coniferous ones retain foliage throughout the year and grow new leaves or needles before losing the old ones.

2. Share with students the Project BudBurst website and a sampling of maps on the FieldScope site. Explain that they will be collecting data in the spring to contribute to this national database. Have them explore these websites, looking at maps and summaries from previous years for species of interest.

3. Ask students, "What is citizen science?"

   Citizen science *refers to efforts in which volunteers participate in scientific research by collecting and/or analyzing data in a common data set. In Project BudBurst, volunteers observe plants and submit data online for use by other volunteers as well as professional scientists. See the Background Information section of this lesson and Chapter 1, "What Is Citizen Science?" for more information.*

4. Discuss information in terms of climate change. Are you noticing any trends in your area? The NOAA website is a good source of climate data across the country (*www.climate.gov*).

5. If possible, bring in winter twigs for students to cut apart, observe, and sketch and label in their science notebooks. This provides practice in closely observing twigs before they conduct their outdoor observations.

Explore

1. Tell students that they will be conducting a descriptive investigation in winter to address one of these questions:

    -   What do twigs on [name of tree or shrub] look like in winter? or

    -   What are the physical characteristics of twigs on [name of tree or shrub] in winter?

2. Take students to the site and have them use the provided data sheets to:

    -   Record date, time, place, and air temperature.

    -   Draw and label a twig on the tree or shrub.

    -   Use a magnifier to observe twig details and label the new observations using a circle to indicate magnification.

    -   Write a description of their twig, using terms in their labeled drawing.

    -   Record the growth that occurred during last year's growing season, measuring from the twig tip to the first bud scale scar.

3. Optional: Have students compare their twig to illustrations of that species in a local winter botany identification book.

4. Ask students to write questions they have about their winter twigs.

    For example, they might wonder when the buds will burst open, or which buds will become flowers and which will become leaves. (In some species, like lilac, the flowers and leaves emerge from the same buds. You can build intrigue so they will be eager to continue their observations into the spring.)

Explain

1. Tell students to read a nonfiction page about how buds form and what factors determine when buds will burst (see Additional Resources).

2. Pose systems questions such as these and instruct students to record answers in their science notebooks:

- What are the parts of the twig?

- What are the functions of these parts?

- What would happen if the terminal bud were missing?

- Considering that a twig is a subsystem of a tree, what is the function of a twig within the larger system of the tree?

- When the twig is on a tree or shrub, what are some of the inputs it receives?

  Example inputs include water, sugars produced through photosynthesis, mineral nutrients taken up from the soil.

- What are some of the outputs?

  Example outputs include growth of buds, leaves, or twigs, and transfer of water or sugars to other parts of the plant.

- What would happen if all the twigs fell off or were removed from a tree?

- What factors influence when buds will burst into leaf or flower?

- What might happen to the time when buds burst into leaf if temperature increases?

Elaborate

1. Discuss the importance of accuracy when submitting data to a citizen science site.

   Scientists use citizen science data to make new discoveries about the natural world. Students can submit data and also use the larger online database to make discoveries of their own!

2. Once per month throughout the winter, provide time for students to visit their twig outdoors and record any changes they observe. When spring is approaching, have them read Project BudBurst's article about phenology: *http://budburst.org/science/phenology_defined.php*

3. Have the students review their twig data sheets and discuss protocols they will be following for collecting and recording data as the twig changes in the spring.

4. In the spring, conduct brief daily observations in order to track when the buds first burst into leaf or flower. When this occurs, students can observe their twig within the context of the whole tree or shrub and fill out the data needed submit to Project Budburst and compare their findings with those submitted by others. They can submit a Single Report at this point or begin working on a Regular Report if continued periodic observations will be possible.

Evaluate

1. Arrange for your students to teach students in a lower grade about the parts and identification of their chosen tree or shrub, along with any fun facts they have learned.

2. Have students compare two different types of twigs using Venn diagrams or other graphic organizer and write about the comparison.

3. Ask students to describe the twig as a system including inputs and outputs along with factors that influence bud burst.

4. Ask them to reflect in their science notebooks why it is important to record the timing of buds bursting into leaf or flower.

5. Have students periodically report to the class their continued observations of their twigs. This could be in the form of a science conference held once per month. Students would experience how scientists share ideas with each other and ask questions of each other.

Extend

1. Students could continue observing their twig to submit further data to Project BudBurst, for example indicating when all the leaves have unfolded, the plant is in full flower, or the first fruits have ripened. This would enable them to submit a Regular Report to Project BudBurst.

2. Students could extend their field investigations, going beyond descriptive studies to conduct a comparative investigation. For example, they could address a question such as whether twig growth is slower on northern than southern sides of shrubs or trees, or whether last year's twig growth differed

between two different species of trees. See "Building Field Investigations From Student Questions" (pp. 53–57 in Pacific Education Institute's Field Investigation Guide) for detailed information and data collection forms (see Additional Resources).

Lesson Resource

- How Do Twigs Change Over Time? Data Sheet

Additional Resources

American Forest Foundation. 2012. *Project learning tree: PreK–8 environmental education activity guide*.
Summary: Provides several lessons focusing on trees, such as "Adopt a Tree," "Bursting Buds," "Trees as Habitats," and "Every Tree for Itself"

Burnie, D. 2005. *Tree*. London: DK.
Summary: Includes useful photographs and explanations about trees and tree growth, and page 24 provides great examples of winter twigs

Johnson, S. 1986. *How leaves change*. Minneapolis, MN: Lerner Publications.
Summary: Shares information about growth and changes in leaves throughout the year

Ryken, A. E., P. Otto, K. Pritchard, and K. Owens. 2007. *Field investigations: Using outdoor environments to foster student learning of scientific processes*. Olympia, WA: Pacific Education Institute. *www.pacificeducationinstitute.org/workspace/resources/field-investigation-guide-updated-april-2009.pdf*
Summary: Provides guidance in preparing students to conduct investigations, building field investigations from student questions, and using data collected over time to identify patterns and relationships

How Do Twigs Change Over Time?
Data Sheet

Name:_____

Location of your twig:

Type of tree or bush (if known): _____

Description of the site: _____

Latitude/Longitude: _____

Select a twig to observe closely. Sketch your twig next to this one and label the buds and scars:

(Image source: *www.pacificeducationinstitute.org/workspace/resources/field-investigation-guide- updated-april-2009.pdf*)

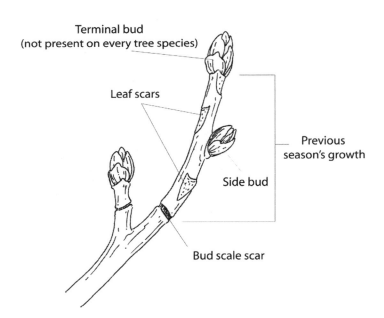

Describe your twig, including the size, shape, and placement of the buds, leaf scars, and bud scale scars:

Measure the length of last season's growth (from the tip to the first bud scale scar:

_____ (in millimeters or centimeters)

Questions about your twig:

I wonder …

I wonder what would happen if …

Flight of the Pollinators

Plant Phenology From a Pollinator's Perspective

by Brian Haggerty, University of California, Santa Barbara,
Alisa Hove, Warren Wilson College,
Susan Mazer, University of California, Santa Barbara, and
LoriAnne Barnett, USA National Phenology Network,
with assistance from UCSB undergraduates Harrison Abry, Sara Healey, and Laurel Phelps

Overview

Students learn how to observe, quantify, and record how plants change across seasons. They participate in a nationwide citizen science effort to track phenology (seasonal change) and study the effects of climate change on plants and animals. Applying these concepts to conservation issues, they consider supporting pollinator diversity in the local landscape by planting phenologically diverse gardens.

Big Idea

Seasonal variations in climate influence plant life cycles, with consequent impacts on the availability of resources for various pollinators.

Citizen Science Connection

Nature's Notebook (www.usanpn.org)

Time Required/Location

Two 50-minute class sessions, one indoors and one outdoors. The activity can be repeated as often as desired over the seasons.

Learning Objectives

Students will be able to:

- Recognize the sequence of reproductive events that lead to seed production in most species of flowering plants

- Identify pollinator syndromes and predict which pollinator(s) are likely to visit the flowers of any plant species they come across

- Identify simple methods for helping to conserve local pollinator diversity across the seasons

- Contribute observation data to the Nature's Notebook citizen science project

- Interpret the ecological significance of plant reproductive phenology for plants, pollinators, and animals that consume the resulting fruits and seeds

Resources Needed

- Computer with internet access

- Smartboard or projector

- Pollination Syndrome Guide (1 per student or group, see sample provided)

- Flight of the Pollinators Data Sheet (1 per student or group, see sample provided)

- Plant species ID guide, visual aids, or signs

- Journals or paper for journaling activity

- Clipboards

- Hand lenses and magnifying glasses

- Cameras (optional)

Background Information

The conservation of plant species requires the availability of pollinators that are abundant when the plants are in flower, just as the conservation of pollinators requires that the flowers they feed on are available and abundant. Through the Nature's Notebook citizen science project, scientists, students, and others are learning about the influence of climate on plants and pollinators. The more complete the data set becomes, the higher its value for research and decision making in fields such as natural resource management, agriculture, and health. Participation can occur in school yards, urban green spaces, or larger natural areas such as wild-life refuges and parks. This lesson is adapted from a longer unit (Haggerty, Hove, Mazer, and Barnett 2012). A 13-minute video at *www.usanpn.org/about* provides further information about phenology and citizen science.

Conducting the Activity

Engage

1. Activate awareness of phenology by exploring students' connections with the seasons. For example, the discussion could focus on:

   - Nearby plants: What's happening with the plants in your neighborhood or school yard right now? Are they actively producing new leaves, or are the leaves changing their colors or aging?

   - Seasonal human health: Does anyone suffer from seasonal allergies, and at what times of year? When do mosquitoes emerge and begin to bite? In what seasons do colds and flu spread quickly?

   - Sports and outdoor activities: What sports are played each spring? Summer? Fall? Winter? Do nearby trees have leaves on them during those sports?

2. Follow with questions such as these about the seasonal availability of food:

   - What foods are currently in season or ready to harvest locally?

   - Which are you looking forward to in the coming season?

   - What season comes to mind for tomatoes, peaches, berries, and pumpkins?

3. Finally, connect students' awareness of their food with pollination. Reinforce their knowledge that fruits and seeds develop from pollinated (and fertilized) flowers.

   The critical point is that the peaches and berries that are ripe today started as flowers that were pollinated by an animal weeks prior. Similarly, flowers that are visible today represent the future food supply for birds, deer, bears, caterpillars, squirrels, and many other animals, including humans.

4. Consider discussing one or more of these additional questions:

    *   What is pollination? (*Transfer of pollen from anthers (male pollen-producing structures) to stigma (female pollen-receiving structure); this can happen between flowers on different plants, between flowers on one plant, or even within one flower.*)

    *   What is a pollinator? (*An animal that carries pollen from anthers to stigma.*)

    *   Why do pollinators visit flowers? (*Usually to obtain food, including nectar or pollen.*)

    *   What attracts pollinators to specific types of flowers? (*Some plants have brightly colored blossoms, or ones with patterns of contrasting colors to attract pollinators. Others produce scents. Some of the earliest spring blooms such as skunk cabbage and Jack in the Pulpit produce heat that attracts insects.*)

    *   Who is a pollinator? (*Name as many as possible—bees, butterflies, birds, moths, flies, beetles, bats, rodents and so on.*)

    *   What types of flowers attract each type of pollinator? (*For example, hummingbirds are attracted to red, tube-shaped flowers. Think about how pollinators are attracted to a combination of traits in flowers, including color, structure, and reward.*)

Explore[1]

1. Explore the concept of phenology from a pollinator's perspective by actively searching for and identifying pollination syndromes—these are flower traits such as size, shape, color, and scent that collectively tend to attract and offer rewards to a particular type of pollinator or suite of pollinators.

2. To prepare students for their time outdoors, share the Pollination Syndrome Guide and discuss the types of floral features needed by various types of pollinators. Then have students use this guide while exploring your school yard or other outdoor area and record information on the data sheet. You could

---

1. Be aware of any students who may have allergies to bee stings. Follow your school's prescribed safety guidelines.

organize students into groups according to pollinator type (bee group, moth group, and so on) or groups containing one of each pollinator type (such as a bee, a moth, a butterfly, and a hummingbird). Tell students they will be taking the perspective of pollinators as they explore the school yard.

3. Ask, "What is citizen science?"

    Citizen science *refers to efforts in which volunteers partner with professional scientists to collect or analyze data. Through the USA National Phenology Network's Nature's Notebook citizen science project, scientists monitor the influence of climate on the phenology of plants, animals, and landscapes. See Chapter 1, "What Is Citizen Science?" for more information.*

4. To align this activity with species targeted by the Nature's Notebook citizen science project (*www.usanpn.org*), use the "Participate" tab to learn which of the targeted plant species occur in your region. If you are unfamiliar with the species at your site, you could consult with the local chapter of your state's Native Plant Society or agricultural extension service or with nearby botanic gardens, natural reserves, nurseries, or native plant landscapers.

    Decide how you would like to organize the students' data collection. Possibilities include:

    -   Each pollinator/student records his/her own observations (using the data sheet provided at the end of this lesson plan), or

    -   Pollinator/students work in pairs, with one counting flowers and the other recording the counts, or

    -   Pollinator/students work in groups, with the data sheet passed around and everyone taking turns counting flowers and recording data.

    Students could use a field guide for plant identification, or you could simplify their ID process by bringing samples (including stems, leaves, and flowers) of available species into class before the field day or by labeling selected varieties or flagging particular plants in the field for them to identify.

5. Go to your outdoor site and instruct students to keep an eye out for pollinators and observe how they interact with flowers. Describe the kinds of observations to make, such as:

- Are the flower visitors drinking nectar, collecting pollen, and/or eating pollen?

- Do the visitors crawl inside the flower, stay perched on top, or hover in front?

- Do they tend to visit several flowers on the same plant, or just one flower per plant?

- After a pollinator visits a flower, can you see pollen deposited on the stigma, or can you see signs that pollen was removed?

From the perspective of a pollinator, ask students to consider the following questions for each flowering plant that they visit:

- Are you the right type of pollinator for this plant? Why or why not?

- What characteristics of the flowers on this plant are attractive to you as a pollinator?

- What pollinators would you expect to find visiting this plant?

Explain

Back in the classroom, engage students in a discussion about their observations and results. Construct a summary data table using everyone's data, and then ask students to construct graphs (examples provided in the detailed lesson online). Topics for discussion could include:

- *Observations of real pollinators:* Did anyone see real pollinators? What were they doing? How did they interact with flowers? Were some types of pollinators more abundant than others?

- *Analyzing and interpreting data:* Which type of pollinator has the fewest flowers available today? (In other words, which type of pollination syndrome is NOT represented among today's flowers?) Is this because their plants haven't flowered yet or have finished flowering? Do you predict that more flowers will soon become available for the types of pollinators that have few flowers available today (i.e., are flower buds present)? For each type of pollinator that you saw, were suitable flowers available for it to visit?

- *Human influence:* Is this area intensely managed or relatively wild? Are plants being watered and if so, might that influence the number of flowers or the number of pollinators observed?

- *Potential extension questions:*

  o How is pollination different from fertilization?

    Pollination is the deposition of pollen on a flower's stigma; fertilization occurs when the sperm carried by a pollen grain fertilizes an egg in an ovule at the base of a flower, enabling the ovule to develop into a seed.

  o What do you know about the global pollinator crisis?

    See the Xerces Society website for information on this topic.

Elaborate

1. Consider having your students enter their observation data into the Nature's Notebook citizen science database. Viewing the data there allows you to review submissions, check for accuracy, and discuss with the group any discrepancies. You also could discuss the importance of accurate data collection for use in scientific climate change research.

2. If your classes repeat their observations over multiple dates, students can graph the availability of blooms across seasons to visualize trends in food available to pollinators. If they identify the species of flowering plants that they observe, they could graph species-specific timing of blooms and illustrate progression of food sources for pollinators across the season (examples provided in the detailed lesson online).

Evaluate

Depending on the level of involvement of your class, you might consider any of the following assessment options:

- Students submit observation notes from the Explore portion of this lesson.

- Students write personal summaries of the class discussion from the Explain portion of this lesson with prompt questions such as: "Define pollination" or "Based on our discussion of how pollinators' form correlates with their pollination function, describe the pollinator form and function associated with specific types of flowers that we observed today."

- Students write detailed essays interpreting the ecological significance of plant reproductive phenology for plants, pollinators, and animals that consume the resulting fruits and seeds.

- Students write a story about "A Day in the Life of a Pollinator" from the perspective of a single pollinator type, describing the sequence of events that lead to successful reproduction. Digital stories could be created using online tools. (A search for "digital story tools" will reveal many different possibilities for doing this.)

- Students answer matching test questions demonstrating their ability to identify pollinator syndromes and predict which pollinator(s) are likely to visit the flowers of particular plant species.

- Students answer lab practice questions by looking at flower samples, listing potential pollinators for each, and describing how each flower might attach each pollinator.

Extend

1. Create opportunities for students to analyze their data within the context of broader trends. For example, they could compare their results to those from nearby sites or from the same site in previous years and interpret the meaning of any trends that are found.

2. Consider planting native species or cultivating a garden in your schoolyard to support pollinators across seasons. On any given day, pollinator diversity in a garden or landscape may range from low to high—we can begin to measure this by identifying the types of pollinator syndromes that are represented by the plants in flower. Cultivating a garden in which the plant species represent several pollination syndromes throughout the season is one way to make a simple and significant contribution to pollinator conservation.

Lesson Resources

- Pollination Syndrome Guide

- Flight of the Pollinators Data Sheet

On the Web

- North American Pollinator Protection Campaign (*www.pollinator.org*): Includes downloadable guides on selecting plants for pollinators, customized by ecoregion

- The Xerces Society, an international nonprofit organization dedicated to protecting wildlife through the conservation of invertebrates and their habitats (*www.xerces.org*): Provides fact sheets on the importance of pollinators and simple steps for conservation of bees and butterflies

- U.S. Forest Service, Celebrating Wildflowers (*www.fs.fed.us/wildflowers/pollinators*): The Pollinators section includes information and advice about gardening for pollinators

Reference

Haggerty, B., A. Hove, S. Mazer, and L. Barnett. 2012. *Flight of the pollinators: A repeatable hands-on exploration of plant phenology from a pollinator's perspective*. USA National Phenology Network and University of California, Santa Barbara. *www.usanpn.org/education*

Additional Resources

Buchmann, S. L., and G. P. Nabhan. 1997. *The forgotten pollinators*. Washington, DC: Island Press/Shearwater Books.
Summary: Explores the relationship between plants and the bees, beetles, butterflies, hummingbirds, moths, bats, and other animals they depend on for reproduction, and discusses connections between endangered species and threatened habitats

Magney, T., K. Eitel, J. Eitel, V. Jansen, J. Schon, R. Rittenburg, and L. Vierling. 2013. Keeping a (digital) eye on nature's clock. *The Science Teacher* 80 (1): 37–43. *www.jstor. org/stable/10.1525/bio.2010.60.issue-3*
Summary: Describes student use of digital cameras to monitor plant phenology throughout the school year and share results through Nature's Notebook or other citizen science projects. Includes comparison of leaf color change detected by the human eye versus image analysis software

Mayer, A. 2010. Phenology and citizen science. *BioScience* 60 (3): 172–175.
Summary: Describes ways in which volunteers have documented seasonal events for the past 100 years and how scientific studies are making use of these long-term data.

Proctor, M. C. F., P. Yeo, and A. Lack. 2003. *The natural history of pollination*. Portland, OR: Timber Press.
Summary: Describes the array of amazing adaptations through which birds, bats, other animals and insects interact with plants and spread pollen to flowers

Pollination Syndrome Guide*

Each cell shows the floral features preferred by the pollinator indicated at the top of the column.

	Bats	Bees	Beetles	Birds	Butterflies	Flies	Humming-birds	Moths
Color of flowers or other attractive structures	White, green, or purple	Bright white, yellow, blue, or UV	White or green	Scarlet, orange, red, or white	Bright, including yellow, red, and purple	Pale /dull to dark brown and purple; flecked with trans-lucent patches	Red mostly, but also orange or yellow	Pale and dull red, purple, pink, or white
Nectar guide	Absent	Present	Absent	Absent	Present	Absent	Absent	Absent
Odor	Strong musty, emitted at night	Fresh, mild, pleasant	None to strongly fruity or foul	None to slight	Faint but fresh	Putrid	None to slight	Strong, fresh, sweet; emitted at night
Nectar	Abundant, somewhat hidden	Usually present	Some-times present, not hidden	Ample, deeply hidden	Ample, deeply hidden	Usually absent	Abundant, deeply hidden	Ample, deeply hidden
Pollen	Ample	Limited to ample, often sticky, scented	Ample	Modest; anthers dangle outside flower	Limited	Limited	Ample; anthers dangle outside flower	Limited
Flower shape	Bowl-shaped; closed during day	Shallow to tubular, with landing platform	Small to large; bowl-like	Large, tubular to cup; strong perch support	Narrow tube with spur; wide landing pad	Shallow; funnel-like or complex with trap	Large, tubular to bell-shaped; no landing platform	Regular, tubular without a lip

*Adapted from North American Pollinator Protection Campaign (www.pollinator.org)

NATIONAL SCIENCE TEACHERS ASSOCIATION

Flight of the Pollinators
Data Sheet

Name (s): _____

What type of pollinator are you? _____

Date: _____ Location: _____

Plant name:

Is this plant on the Nature's Notebook list of currently monitored plants?	___ Yes ___ No
If yes, indicate here when these observations have been entered online:	

Do you see...	Presence (circle one)		Abundance* (circle one)						
Flowers or flower buds	Y	N ?	How many?	< 3	3–10	11– 100	101–1,000	1,001–10,000	> 10,000
Open flowers	Y	N ?	What % of fresh flowers is open?	< 5%	5–24%	25–49%	50–74%	75–94%	≥95%
Fruits (unripe as well as ripe ones)	Y	N ?	How many?	< 3	3–10	11–100	101–1,000	1,001–10,000	> 10,000
Ripe fruits	Y	N ?	What % are ripe?	< 5%	5–24%	25–49%	50–74%	75–94%	≥95%
Recent fruit or seed drop	Y	N ?	How many have recently fallen?	< 3	3–10	11–100	101–1,000	1,001–10,000	> 10,000

* Numerical categories for estimating abundance are from USA-NPN phenological data collection sheets

Ozone Bio-Monitoring Garden Study

by Susan Sachs, Great Smoky Mountains National Park

Overview

Students learn about the effects of ground-level ozone pollution on plants and how that relates to animals. Using an online training module, they practice estimating the amount of damage to plant leaves. They submit plant damage data to an online database and possibly set up an ozone-monitoring garden. This lesson is adapted from activities developed through the Parks as Classrooms project of Great Smoky Mountains National Park (Ladd and Sachs 2011) and can be implemented in any part of the country.

Learning Objectives

Students will be able to:

• Describe what ground-level ozone is and how it affects plants and animals

• Estimate the percentage of leaf injury and evaluate their own estimation error tendencies using images of the leaves of various plant species

Big Idea

Ground-level ozone is a common but invisible air pollutant that injures plants and affects the health of humans and other animals. The levels of ozone pollution can be monitored by periodically checking how certain plant species are reacting to ozone exposure.

Citizen Science Connection

Hands on the Land, Ozone Bio-monitoring (*www.handsontheland.org/environmental-monitoring/ozone-bio-monitoring.html*)

Time Required/Location

45 minutes, indoors
60 minute, outdoors for a survey of school yard plants, or 1 day to prepare garden plot and put in plants (if you wish to establish a garden)
45 minutes, outdoors every two weeks for plant inspection or whenever feasible

- Use vocabulary associated with estimating ozone damage to plants (stippling, chlorosis, necrosis)

- Collect ozone damage data from a specific plant species

Resources Needed

- Computer with internet access

- Projector or interactive whiteboard

- Ozone monitoring plant species and garden plot (optional)

- Data sheets

- Clipboards

Background Information

Ozone is a colorless, highly reactive gas made up of three atoms of oxygen (O_3). Ozone high up in the atmosphere protects living things on Earth from harmful ultraviolet rays. However, ozone that forms close to the Earth's surface is harmful to plants and animals. This ground-level ozone is a widespread air pollutant and the main component of smog. It is created when emissions from power plants, vehicles, and factories combine in the presence of sunlight. This type of ozone is created by chemical reactions between oxides of nitrogen and volatile organic compounds in the presence of sunlight. The effects can have adverse impacts on ecosystems, including loss of species diversity. (For further background, see Ladd and Sachs 2011.)

Conducting the Activity

Engage

Bring in leaves from the school yard that show several types of damage, such as yellowing, turning brown, spotted, or chewed, and have the class brainstorm possible causes. Introduce the idea that some leaf damage is caused by ozone pollution and that we can use leaf condition to study changing ozone levels. Talk about human health conditions associated with surface ozone.

Explore

1. Explain that leaves can have several types of injury: chlorosis (yellowing), purple or brownish dots (stippling), and necrosis (death of leaf tissue). Ozone injury appears as stippling and can be differentiated from other brown spots on leaves by noticing that the damage doesn't cross over any leaf veins, only appears on the upper leaf surface and is more severe at the bottom of a plant.

2. Use the National Park Service's online training module to help students develop skill in evaluating the percent of injury on ozone-sensitive leaves (*www.nature.nps.gov/air/edu/O3Training/index.cfm*). In a computer lab, students could work through this training alone or in groups. If you have a single computer in the classroom, just project the images and work through the module as a class. Decide on the number of practice leaves that you want to use. Have students estimate the percent of the entire leaf surface that appears injured. Note that even though ozone does not damage veins, veins do count in the overall percentage of the leaf. You could create a worksheet similar to the following:

Which species of ozone-sensitive plant did you use? _____

Trial 1
_____ 0%   _____ 1%–6%   _____7%–25%   _____ 26%–50%   _____ 51%–75%   _____ 76%–100%

Trial 2
_____ 0%   _____ 1%–6%   _____7%–25%   _____ 26%–50%   _____ 51%–75%   _____ 76%–100%

[Continue in this manner for as many leaves as you desire.]

Overall, did you underestimate or overestimate the amount of ozone damage?

Instruct students to write an "X" in the percentage category that they think is correct. After checking the answer online, they should record an "O" in the percentage category of the correct answer and then click "next image" to continue the training. When finished, they can look over their data sheet to determine their tendency for either underestimating or overestimating the amount of ozone damage. Students also could be encouraged to create notebook entries that include drawings, measurements, and indications of how they refined their estimation skills.

10

Explain

Collect trial results from each student or group and compare with actual percentages.

- Which percentage groups did the class as a whole have the most difficulty with?

- Which were the easiest?

Most people estimate most accurately at the outer extremes. Was this true for your class? This is a good place for you to introduce related concepts of interest, possibly including leaf anatomy, bioindicators, biodiversity, and relationships between ozone and other air pollutants including sulfur dioxide and nitrogen oxides.

Elaborate

Take students on a walk around the school property to identify ozone-sensitive plant species. If you wish to enter your plant observation data into the Ozone Bio-monitoring citizen science database, you will need to assign code numbers to individual plants. You can study data and graphs from other schools or register your own school at the Hands on the Land site (contact the website administrator to register your school site). Data collection typically begins once new leaves have been established and continues about every two weeks until after the first frost (if appropriate in your area) or until the plant goes to seed. Follow these steps during each data-collection session:

- Measure the plant's total height in centimeters by measuring the distance from the ground to the bottom of the highest, most open leaf. Once the plant is flowering, hold the plant straight and measure to the top of the tallest bloom.

- Count the total number of leaves coming off of the main stem including any missing leaves (indicated by leaf scars).

- Indicate whether the plant is in bud or flower.

- Estimate the percentage of visible ozone damage on the bottom eight leaves.

- Note any other observations such as insect damage or mold.

Ask students, "What is citizen science?"

Citizen science refers to efforts in which volunteers partner with professional scientists to collect or analyze data. Through the

Ozone Monitoring Project, citizen scientists collect data that helps scientists to understand implications for environmental conditions and how changing ozone levels affect plant growth. Researchers have found that even though ground-level ozone levels are improving in some areas, there is still severity of symptoms on plants being noticed. See Chapter 1, "What Is Citizen Science?" for more information.

Evaluate

Ask students to create a news story similar to a weather report to relate their findings on ground-level ozone in your area. Encourage students to use the appropriate scientific vocabulary learned in this lesson. Based on their plant investigations, how high are the ozone levels and why is this a matter of interest to the community? Make sure that students provide important contextual information such as:

- The definition of ground-level ozone and how it affects plants and animals

- A summary of how they collected and interpreted their data

Extend

Consider planting a garden that you can use for long term ozone monitoring. Some common species are cutleaf coneflower (*Rudbeckia laciniata*), crownbeard (*Verbesina occidentalis*), and common milkweed (*Asclepias syriaca*), and other suggested species are identified on this list: *www.fws.gov/refuges/AirQuality/docs/BaltFinalReport1.pdf*. A local gardening club may be able to lend assistance in identifying your school yard plants or developing a garden. This study could also lead into discussions about ways to reduce ground-level ozone production.

Reference

Ladd, I., and S. Sachs. 2011. *Using sensitive plants as bioindicators of ground level ozone pollution*. Purchase Knob, NC: Appalachian Highlands Science Learning Center, Great Smoky Mountains National Park. *www.handsontheland.org/environmental-monitoring/ozone-bio-monitoring.html*

Additional Resource

Bricker, P. L., S. Sachs, and R. Binkley. 2010. Using citizen scientists to measure the effects of ozone damage on native wildflowers. *Science Scope* 33 (8): 12–19.
Summary: Provides sample data sheets and assessment rubrics.

Turtle Trackers

by Jill Nugent, Texas Tech University

Overview

Students learn about turtle species by researching common native turtles, constructing a class field guide of these species, and engaging in one of the regional citizen science projects across the United States that involve aquatic and terrestrial turtles.

Learning Objectives

Students will be able to:

- Identify local species of turtles

- Describe the morphology, behavior, and habitat needs of local turtle species

- Describe several ecological pressures on terrestrial and freshwater turtles

Big Idea

Citizen science makes it possible to track turtle distribution and population trends, become aware of limiting factors, and suggest ways to conserve, protect, and restore native turtle populations.

Citizen Science Connection

No national scale citizen science project focuses on turtles, but regional projects can be located using these portals (*www.birds.cornell. edu/citscitoolkit/projects* or *http://scistarter. com*). A few examples include:

- Texas Turtle Watch (*www.fortworthzoo.org/ conservation/fort-worth-zoo-conservation- highlights/texas-turtle-watch*)

- The Carolina Herp Atlas (*www. carolinaherpatlas.org*)

- Massachusetts Turtle Atlas (*www.turtleatlas. org/atlas/roadkill_hotspot.html*)

- Arkansas Box Turtle Survey (*www. naturalheritage.com/citizen-science/ past_projects/box_turtle.aspx*)

- San Francisco, California (*www. marinwater.org/controller?action=menucli ck&id=584*)

Time Required/Location

Three 45-minute periods, indoors, and variable outdoor experiences

_11_

Resources Needed

- Computer with internet access

- Projector or interactive whiteboard

- Local reptile field guides

- Hand-held GPS units

- Turtle shells (available from *www.nature-watch.com*, or simulated ones created from Styrofoam bowls)

- Relevant data sheets (depending on the project chosen)

- Clipboards

- Access to a pond, small lake, or river that has aquatic turtles

- Binoculars (optional)

Background Information

See Chapter 6, "Case Study: Amphibians and Reptiles," for background information and stories about student turtle investigations and citizen science.

Conducting the Activity

Engage

1. Introduce students to common local aquatic turtle species using a citizen science project website (like those mentioned above) or regional field guides and websites that highlight species found in your state, such as these sites for Texas (*www.texasturtles.org*) and North Carolina (*www.herpsofnc.org*). If the guides or websites include range maps, students could generate their own list of species that might likely be found in the area of the school.

2. Ask students, "What is citizen science?" and discuss its importance in determining the species and numbers of turtles living in ponds and wetlands.

   Citizen science *refers to efforts in which volunteers partner with professional scientists to collect or analyze data. Baseline information about turtle populations is needed in making informed management decisions for turtle protection, but professional scientists* *cannot conduct widespread monitoring without the help of citizen scientists. Through projects such as those listed above, citizen scientists monitor aquatic turtle populations more frequently, over longer time frames, and over larger geographic areas than professional scientists could possibly manage on their own. Both students and professional scientists can use the data posted online in analyzing population trends. See Chapter 1, "What Is Citizen Science?" for more information about citizen science.*

Explore

Option 1: Have students study turtle shells and make sketches in their notebooks. Remind them of the importance of accuracy. Using print or electronic sources, have them label their sketches with features such as marginal scutes, vertebral scutes, pleural scutes, nuchal scutes (on the carapace) and the names of the various plates on the plastron. Some good internet resources are: *www.peteducation.com/article.cfm?c=17+1797&aid=2700* and *www.reptilesofaz.org/Turtles.html*

Option 2: Have students create turtle shell models from Styrofoam bowls. Using shell diagrams from the links in Option 1 as a guide, draw the carapace scute borders on one bowl and the plastron scute borders on another bowl. Cut the plastron bowl to size, which will depend on species. Staple the two pieces together in the area that would be the bridge (see Figure 11.1). As in option 1, have students make and label sketches.

Explain

Share natural history information about the aquatic turtle species common in your area. Also lead a

FIGURE 11.1.

Turtle shells made from Styrofoam bowls, with plastron on the left and carapace on the right

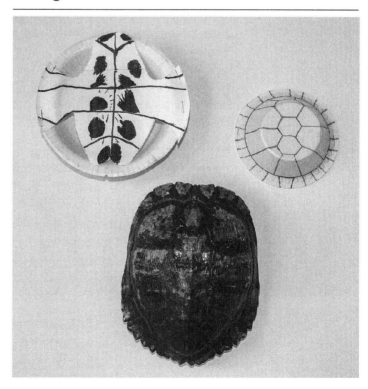

discussion about the ecological role of turtles and the pressures that some turtle populations are facing.

> *For example, the commercial trade is responsible for many turtles being taken out of wild populations for use as pets, food, or medicine. In addition, non-native species sold as pets often get released into the wild by pet owners who have decided they no longer want to care for them. An internet search for "Asian turtle trade" will bring up a variety of reports and news publications. Another pressure is road mortality. Both terrestrial and aquatic turtles move across roads during breeding seasons and often become victims of roadkill.*

Elaborate

Consider these three ways to monitor aquatic turtles, determine whether an appropriate citizen science project exists in your area, and download the relevant datasheets. Select from these monitoring methods:

1. *Observing basking turtles.* Select a pond, lake, or river to monitor. Basking turtles are most active in warm weather in the middle of the day. Upon arrival at your site, find a good position from which to observe. If some students have binoculars, the search range can be wider. As students observe turtles, have them describe to the rest of the class the distinguishing characteristics that identify this turtle species. Record the GPS location of your site.

2. *Trapping and releasing turtles.* (Before beginning any turtle trapping project, first check with your state wildlife commission about regulations related to turtles.) Turtle hoop traps can be purchased from Memphis Net and Twine Company (*www.memphisnet.net/category/traps_animal_turtle*). Traps can be baited with a variety of materials such as canned sardines, chicken, or hot dogs. Students could investigate which bait attracts the most turtles. Care needs to be taken in setting the traps so that captured turtles can rise to the surface to breathe. Another option is to build basking traps that do not need to be baited, using directions obtained through internet search.

3. *Reporting roadkill sightings.* For example, the Massachusetts Turtle Atlas collects data on roadkill turtles in this state: (*www.turtleatlas.org/atlas/roadkill_hotspot.html*).

Evaluate

1. Divide students into small groups and assign each group a turtle species to research. Challenge them to summarize their findings on a single page. They should include the common name, scientific name, and natural history information such as habitat, behavior, life cycle, and how common the turtle is in your area. Assemble these resource sheets to create a class field guide to your local aquatic turtle species.

2. Working in groups, have students create an infomercial about ecological pressures on terrestrial and freshwater turtles.

Extend

1. Consider inviting a guest speaker to discuss turtle conservation efforts in your area. Possibilities include staff from a zoo, aquarium, or museum or a wildlife biologist, herpetologist, naturalist, biology professor or graduate student.

2. Explore the outputs of turtle tracking citizen science projects in other parts of the country to compare their findings with yours. Example projects are listed in the Citizen Science Connection and Additional Resources sections of this lesson.

3. Suggest that students embark on a public awareness campaign related to the detrimental release of pet turtles. The Turtle Survival Alliance provides some excellent ideas and advice.

On the Web

-   Arkansas Natural Heritage Commission (*www.naturalheritage.com/!userfiles/ 2007_Box_Turtle_Results.pdf*): Information about turtle conservation and findings from a box turtle survey conducted through citizen science

-   Citizen Science Central (*www.birds.cornell.edu/citscitoolkit*): A portal for searching citizen science projects by topic and/or location

-   Neighborhood Box Turtle Watch (*naturalsciences.org/research-collections/citizen-science/neighborhood-box-turtle-watch*): Advice about how to make your neighborhood turtle-friendly and information about how to document box turtle sightings with minimal stress to the turtles

-   SciStarter (*www.scistarter.com*): A portal for searching citizen science projects by topic and/or location

- Texas Turtle Watch: A citizen science program for tomorrow's turtles (*www.fortworthzoo. org/wp-content/uploads/2011/05/TexasTurtleWatch-TrainingGuide_Curriculum.pdf*): A curriculum packet with background information and lesson plans for middle school learning experiences related to turtles, including classroom activities and ideas for testable questions to investigate in the field

- Turtle Survival Alliance (*www.turtlesurvival.org/resources/how-to-help-turtles*): Ideas about how to keep wild turtles safe and help improve their habitats, as well as advice on responsible care of pet turtles

Additional Resources

Summers, S. 2012. Turtle conservation and citizen science, a winning combination for your classroom. *Science Scope* 36 (3): 33–38.
Summary: Discussion of multiyear field research by middle school classes on the impact of invasive turtles on native species.

Who's Out There?

A Calling Amphibian Survey

by Terry M. Tomasek, Elon University, and Jill Nugent, Texas Tech University

Overview

Students learn how to identify frogs and toads by call and apply this knowledge during a frog call hike to inventory calling amphibians and analyze call patterns within the context of atmospheric and habitat conditions.

Learning Objectives

Students will be able to:

- Use citizen science data to determine local species of calling amphibians

- Distinguish calling amphibian species by listening to calls

- Describe relationships among calling patterns, weather, and habitat condition

- Define niche partitioning

- Explain the mechanism for sound production by frogs

- Explain the role of frog calling behavior in population survival

Big Idea

Worldwide populations of frogs and toads are declining, in many cases for unknown reasons. Widespread and long-term monitoring is needed to help unravel this mystery and better understand the status and health of these indicator species and the habitats in which they live and breed.

Citizen Science Connections

- North American Amphibian Monitoring Program (NAAMP) (*www.pwrc.usgs.gov/naamp*)

- FrogWatch USA (*www.aza.org/frogwatch*)

Time Required/Location

Two 60-minute indoor sessions with one 2-hour field experience in between

Resources Needed

- Computer with internet access and speakers

- Interactive whiteboard or projector

- Frog call recordings

- Instrumentation for measuring air temperature and relative humidity

- Calling Amphibian Survey Data Sheet (1 per student or group)

- Clipboards for data sheets (1 per student or group)

- Cameras and/or audio recording devices (optional)

Background Information

See Chapter 6, "Case Study: Amphibians and Reptiles," for background information and stories about student involvement in amphibian surveys and citizen science. Monitoring of frog and toad calls by citizen scientists provides data that are crucial in tracking their population status and health, which are in decline worldwide due to habitat loss, the deadly chrytrid fungus, and other factors. The calling behavior of frogs and toads can tell scientists something about the makeup of local populations as well as each species' relative abundance. Frogs and toads produce calls for many reasons: to attract a mate (only males call), to announce territory, to signal an alarm to other animals, and to indicate a release when grasped by another male.

Students studying frog and toad calls can also learn about the physics of sound. The calls are produced through a combination of voice box, muscles, and vocal sacs. The frog inflates the vocal sacs by filling them with air. The air is then forced across two muscle bands stretched across the voice box causing them to vibrate. Different pitches result when the frog relaxes or tightens the muscles. Air is recycled between the lungs and the air sac.

Conducting the Activity

Engage

1. The term "calling amphibian" may not be obvious to students. Begin with a class discussion of the idea that not all amphibians communicate with sounds we can hear (frogs and toads do, but salamanders do not). Talk about how and why frogs call.

2. Share state-level calling amphibian data with your class by showing a species detection map for your state from the NAAMP website. Explain that NAAMP coordinators randomly generated survey routes in each state. In some states, the routes were then ground-truthed to identify stops along the route that were in potential amphibian breeding areas (wetlands, ponds, and streams). Volunteers survey each route an average of three times per year during breeding seasons, listening for species-specific vocalizations. A measure of abundance is determined for each species. Volunteers also record environmental parameters such as air temperature, relative humidity, wind and sky condition, rainfall amounts, moon phase, and noise factor. Ask students, "What is citizen science?"

Citizen science *refers to efforts in which volunteers partner with professional scientists to collect or analyze data. Through NAAMP, citizen scientists help scientists by reporting distribution and relative abundance of calling amphibians in a wider geographic area than would be possible by the scientists themselves. This allows scientists (and students) to better understand regional and national trends in frog distributions and in changes in frog populations. Understanding these trends will provide not only a better understanding of the status and health of our frog and toad populations but a picture of the health of the habitats where these animals live and breed. Having this type of long-term knowledge is an important step in enabling us to protect critical habitats. See Chapter 1 for more information about citizen science.*

3. Find the earliest map for a given species (this will be the first year that your state participated in NAAMP). If your state does not currently participate in NAAMP, use the map from a neighboring state. As students study these maps, collectively generate a list of calling amphibians common to your school's community.

Explore

1. Show pictures of common calling amphibians in your community and play the calls of each. Use state-specific web pages, books with recordings or national web pages suggested below. Help students identify distinguishing characteristics of calls for each species. This video might be of particular interest because it was made by a young person and contains excellent footage of frogs calling: *www.youtube.com/watch?v=jA_eHVxprdI*

LESSON 12
Who's Out There? A Calling Amphibian Survey

2. Review the data sheet (see end of lesson) and provide any needed instruction on how to read weather instruments.

3. Arrange for a frog call hike. Scientific protocols for conducting calling amphibian surveys can be found on the NAAMP website. These modifications are suggested for middle or high school students:

   • Select a route on school property or a local park. Identify stops near appropriate frog habitat. The number of stops identified depends on the length of time desired to complete the survey.

   • Calling amphibian surveys typically begin 30 minutes after sunset. However, some species of frogs can be heard calling during the school day.

   • Students begin at the first identified stop by recording atmospheric conditions (temperature, humidity, sky code, wind code, moon phase). They then quietly listen for a designated amount of time (the NAAMP protocol suggests five minutes, but two minutes of listening is recommended for students). After the listening period is complete, students discuss what species of frogs they heard and determine a calling index: 1–individuals can be counted, with space between calls; 2–some overlapping calls; 3–full chorus calls that are constant, continuous, and overlapping. Once all data are recorded, the group moves on to any subsequent stops.

Explain

1. Upon returning to the classroom, ask students to share the data they collected. If the class separated into groups, each group could share their findings while others make comparisons.

2. Ask "Why did we hear some common species and not others?" (Lead a discussion about breeding seasons and niche partitioning).

3. Show pictures of freshwater environments (i.e., ephemeral pools, lakes, streams). Explain how and why calling amphibians use these types of environments. Introduce the concept of amphibians as bio-indicators of environmental quality.

LESSON 12
Who's Out There? A Calling Amphibian Survey

12

Elaborate

1. Have students take the public frog call quiz provided by USGS Patuxent Wildlife Research Center (*www.pwrc.usgs.gov/frogquiz*). Ask them to:

    *   Select your state from the drop-down menu, look at the list of calling amphibians found there, and use the "Frog Call Lookup" function to review any they do not know.

    *   Take the quiz, listening to calls and answering multiple-choice questions about what species they have heard.

    *   Note their detection index, and retake the quiz if they would like more practice. The quiz is scored by *correct responses minus misidentifications divided by total possible correct identifications*.

2. Participate in FrogWatch by submitting frog call data to *www.aza.org/frogwatch-monitoring-protocols*

Evaluate

1. Have students make an online local field guide for the calling amphibians in the survey area, using free wiki software. Students could share the link for this website with other school-age students and families and with the local library or other community gathering place. For assessment of lesson learning objectives, the field guide should contain the following information:

    *   Names of local calling amphibians and a map of where they were heard

    *   If students took cameras on the field trip, they could attach pictures of the animals.

    *   If students took audio recording equipment, they could also attach audio files of the actual frog calls.

    *   A description of their frog call survey procedures and their findings including relationships among calling patterns, weather conditions and habitat condition. They should also provide a description of what this type of survey does not reveal or limitations of this type of scientific investigation.

    *   A description of calling phenology. When different species call at different times of year and why this might be important for niche partitioning.

LESSON 12
Who's Out There? A Calling Amphibian Survey

- An explanation for the mechanism of sound production by frogs and the role of frog calling behavior in population survival.

2. You could evaluate student scientific practice skills by checking their student data sheets for accuracy and by quizzing on identification of recorded sounds of local frog species.

Extend

1. Hold a class discussion on questions such as these:

   - Why monitor frogs and toads?

     This data provides valuable information about the status and health of local frog and toad species. Worldwide populations are on the decline, in many cases for unknown reasons. Long-term monitoring is needed to better understand these changes.

   - What are potential causes of frog and toad population declines?

     Habitat loss, habitat degradation, pollution, disease, introduced or exotic species, and/or global climate change.

2. Place students in groups and have each group create a Venn diagram showing similarities and differences between North American frogs and toads.

   Similarities between toads and frogs include:

   - *Affected by toxins in the water and surrounding environment;*

   - *Call for mates;*

   - *Hibernate or become less active in cold weather months (in northern areas of the world);*

   - *Depend on water or moisture for at least part of the life cycle.*

Differences between toads and frogs include:

- *Toad eggs are typically deposited in strings while frog eggs are deposited in jelly masses*

- *Toads have shorter, less powerful legs than frogs so toads tend to hop while frogs jump*

- *Toads typically have drier, rough, warty looking skin while frogs typically have smooth, moist skin.*

3. Print out and provide characteristics such as those listed below for each student group to think about and sort into characteristics of frog or toad. Students are not limited to these ideas, but these will provide them with ideas to start with, and will get the small group discussion started and focused on task.

   Shape of egg mass: in clumps or in strings?

   Habitat: adults live in or near the water typically live on land?

   Leg length: back legs shorter or longer than front legs?

   Feet: toes webbed or unwebbed?

   Body shape: streamlined and slender or thicker in the middle?

   Skin moisture: moist or relatively dry?

   Skin texture: mostly smooth or rough and warty?

   Parotoid glands: has big bumps on neck behind the eyes or does not have these glands?

   Locomotion: powerful jumpers or short hoppers?

4. Have a guest speaker familiar with FrogWatch and amphibian monitoring visit the classroom (guest speakers could include a wildlife biologist, master naturalist, local zoo or museum staffer, local college biology professor, herpetologist, or grad student in biology, and so on) and present a session on FrogWatch USA, with an emphasis on the goal of the program and how students can participate in the program.

LESSON 12
Who's Out There? A Calling Amphibian Survey

5. As a wrap-up, read or summarize for students the amazing story of the middle school science class in Minnesota that made a groundbreaking scientific discovery relating to amphibian malformations (*www.pbs.org/strangedays/ educators/season1/ag_tw_ffiles.html*). This information might be used as a call to action to monitor amphibians in your local area!

6. Pick one local amphibian species (such as the cricket frog) and plan to focus on that species to monitor. Record data throughout a school year when the frog calls (e.g., what days of year, what times of day) and under what conditions (e.g., cloud cover, precipitation).

7. Research other native species or nonnative species and their impact on local species.

8. Create a regional or state field guide of native amphibians.

9. Your students might also invite other people in the school community to report to them about frogs they are hearing in their backyards and neighborhoods. Who knows, maybe your class could start their own citizen science project in your local school district!

Lesson Resource

• Calling Amphibian Survey Data Sheet

On the Web

• Animal Diversity Website (*http://animaldiversity.ummz.umich.edu/site/topics/frogCalls. html*): Information about calling amphibians and sound files for sample calls

Calling Amphibian Survey Data Sheet

Observer's Name(s) _____ Date _____ Time (Military) Start: _____ End: _____

Environmental Parameters at Start of Run

Air Temp. ____°C Relative Humidity ____% Wind Code ____ Sky Code ____
Rain amt. w/in last 24 hrs ____ mm # of Days since last rainfall _____ Moon Phase _____

Environmental Parameters at End of Run

Air Temp. ____°C Relative Humidity ____% Wind Code ____ Sky Code ____

Instructions

At each stop listen for 2 minutes (recording start time), then record the air temperature, the amphibian calling index for each species heard, and whether moonlight was visible or not.

		Per Stop Information				
Stop #		1	2	3	4	5
Start Time (Military)						
Air Temperature (°C)						
Species ↓	**Stop # →**	1	2	3	4	5
Moonlight visible: (yes or no)						

Amphibian Calling Index	**Sky Codes**	**Moon Phase**	**Beaufort Wind Codes**
1 = Individuals can be counted; there is space between calls 2 = Calls of individuals can be distinguished but there is some overlapping of calls 3 = Full chorus, calls are constant, continuous, and overlapping	0 = Few clouds 1 = Partly cloudy (scattered) or variable sky 2 = Cloudy or overcast 4 = Fog or smoke 5 = Drizzle or light rain	0 = New 1 = Waxing Crescent 2 = First Quarter 3 = Waxing Gibbous 4 = Full 5 = Waning Gibbous 6 = Last Quarter 7 = Waning Crescent	0 = Calm (< 1 mph) 1 = Light Air (1–3 mph) 2 = Light Breeze (4–7 mph), leaves rustle, can feel wind on face 3 = Gentle Breeze (8–12 mph), leaves and twigs move around, small flag extends DO NOT conduct survey if windier than a 3.

Wetland Discovery

by Terry M. Tomasek, Elon University
and Danielle Marchand, Bridgewater Junior Senior High, Bridgewater, NS

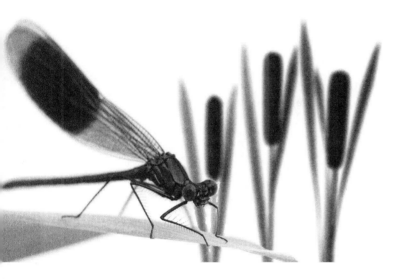

Overview

Students learn about temporary bodies of water and go on a field trip to map this type of wetland habitat and describe the plants and animals living there.

Learning Objectives

Students will be able to:

- Describe the biodiversity associated with temporary pools of water

- Explain the value of temporary pools of water

- Recognize the impact of human decisions on the environment

- Describe how a habitat changes over time and explain the implications for organisms

Big Idea

Ephemeral pools and other seasonal wetlands play vital ecological roles in terms of hydrology and biodiversity and provide critical breeding grounds for a variety of amphibian and invertebrate species that are adapted to life in temporary waters.

Citizen Science Connection

No national scale citizen science project focuses on ephemeral pools, but regional projects can be located using these portals (www.birds.cornell.edu/citscitoolkit/projects or http://scistarter.com). A few examples include:

- Nova Scotia Vernal Pool Mapping and Monitoring Project (www.gov.ns.ca/nse/wetland/vernal.pool.mapping.project.asp)

- Southwest New Hampshire, Ashuelot Valley Environmental Observatory (www.aveo.org/citizen-science/vernal-pools)

- Sonoma County California, Adopt-A-Vernal Pool Endangered Plant Monitoring Project (www.citizen-science.org/Laguna/rdPage.aspx)

- Vermont Vernal Pool Mapping Project (www.vtecostudies.org/VPMP)

- Ohio Vernal Pool Partnership (www.ovpp.org)

- Vernal Pool Association in Massachusetts (www.vernalpool.org/vernal_1.htm)

Time Required/Location

One 60-minute indoor session followed by a 2-hour field trip. Post–field trip sessions are suggested, with length varying depending on options selected.

Resources Needed

- Computer with internet access

- Projector or interactive whiteboard

- "Fill Those Potholes!" article from the USDA Forest Service middle school science education journal, Natural Inquirer (*www.naturalinquirer.org/Fill-Those-Potholes-a-98.html*)

- A field guide to wetland plants

- Wetland animal field guide (For example, *A Field Guide to the Animals of Vernal Pools* by Leo Kenney and Matthew Burne, or check the internet for field guides specific to your location)

- 50 m tape measure

- Meterstick

- Air and water thermometers

- GPS, or GPS app on smart phone

- Clipboards

- A local seasonal wetland

Background Information

Wetlands of all types provide key wildlife habitat. Seasonal wetlands such as ephemeral or vernal pools are often overlooked because they are sometimes nothing more than a depression in the ground that temporarily fills with water. However, these wetlands are particularly valuable because they provide habitat for numerous rare plants and animals that survive as seeds, eggs, or cysts during dry seasons and then grow and reproduce when water becomes available. These pools also support a variety of invertebrates, frogs, and salamanders that can breed nowhere else. A real-life drama unfolds depending on the time of year that water becomes available. For example, visitors to ephemeral pools that fill in the fall in the eastern United States are likely to find marbled salamander eggs hatching. Pools that fill instead in late winter provide breeding grounds for the spotted salamander. In spite of the high ecological value of these seasonal wetlands, they are endangered due to land development and climate change.

Conducting the Activity

Engage

1. Using The Harvard Forest Schoolyard LTER Database (*http://harvardforest2. fas.harvard.edu/asp/hf/ php/k12/k12_graph.php*), show data from one or more schools that have sampled vernal pools. Select "Vernal Pool" in the Project drop-down box and click Submit. Select any school and again click Submit. Select "All" to plot by date. You have the choice of which variable to graph: diameter, depth, air temperature or water temperature. When the graph is generated, you will see how your selected variable changed over time. Try a variety of graphs and discuss trends you observe. You are likely to see decreases in diameter and depth as the pools dry up and increase in water temperature. If time allows, you could assign students to work in small groups to explore other school data and look for trends.

2. Explain that students acting as citizen scientists posted these data and ask, "What is citizen science, and why is it important?"

   Citizen science *refers to efforts in which volunteers partner with professional scientists to collect or analyze data, such as the vernal pool data assembled in Harvard's database. Citizen science projects that focus on temporary wetlands help to raise awareness about the value of these endangered habitats, map their locations, monitor the life they support, and plan appropriate conservation measures. Citizen scientists who map locations of ephemeral pools provide data that is useful in planning conservation measures and awareness campaigns. See Chapter 1, "What Is Citizen Science?" for more information.*

3. Show the video entitled "Restoration Program helps citizen scientists explore local wildlife" (*www.youtube.com/watch?v=M2ckQppONpw*) and engage students in a conversation about temporary pools of water they may have seen around their communities. Ask them:

   - What do you think lives in these pools?

   - What might be the benefit of these pools?

   - Why do you think some people might object to these pools?

Or, if you prefer a more literature-based approach to introducing the topic, have students read "Fill Those Potholes!" (see Resources Needed section of this lesson) and discuss the science described in the article. Make connections between prairie potholes and other types of seasonal pools in your part of the county.

> *Because ephemeral pools are usually devoid of fish, they make excellent breeding grounds for a variety of amphibian and invertebrate species.*

Explore

1. Identify a temporary pool in your area. Help students to generate a list of questions they would like to consider as they plan their ephemeral pool investigation.

2. Take students on a field trip to the site, checking first to see if data sheets are provided by a citizen science project in your region. Have students write a site description, noting the location with a handheld GPS unit, and ask them to take pictures and make sketches. Use a wetland plant guide to identify the vegetation around the pool. Record the following data:

   - diameter of the pool (typically in meters)
   - maximum depth of the water (typically in centimeters)
   - air temperature (typically in degrees Celsius)
   - water temperature (typically in degrees Celsius)
   - other types of organisms (aquatic insects, frogs, salamanders, fairy shrimp)

3. If possible, visit the site several more times to track seasonal changes, and have students create graphs to show selected variables as a function of date.

Explain

After returning from the field trip, provide students the opportunity to share their findings with the rest of the class. As students share, use this time to remind students of how their findings related to key concepts of the water cycle, food webs, and biotic and abiotic factors. Ask them to think about why it could be advantageous for organisms to be adapted to living in such a variable environment, where water may disappear entirely for part of each year (see Background Information section).

Elaborate

Have students work in groups to explore the following questions and prepare a presentation:

- What threatens ephemeral pools? What would happen if these pools disappeared?

- What would we have to do to keep this from happening and why would we bother?

- What is sustainability? Why do we value sustainability and how could we show that we value it?

Other options include creating an ephemeral pool field guide highlighting the organisms found, or a book or e-book explaining the role of biotic and abiotic factors in the ecology of temporary wetlands.

Evaluate

Ask students to reflect on the value of wetlands and why they are worth protecting. This could be in the form of an essay, collage, blog, video, or other format of your choice.

Extend

1. Search for a wetland-related citizen science project in your area (see the Citizen Science Connection section of this lesson). For example, the Vernal Pool Association (*www.vernalpool.org*) is collecting data on migrating amphibians. If you live in Massachusetts, you can submit data to their amphibian roadway crossing database (*http://linkinglandscapes.info/roads/salamander_map.html*). Ducks Unlimited Canada offers a variety of opportunities for school classes to take part in wetland monitoring, stewardship, interpretation, and achieving recognition as a Wetland Centre of Excellence (*www.ducks.ca/education*).

2. Advanced students could read the article by Oscarson and Calhoun (2007) and discuss in small groups. This article will be challenging for middle school students, but guided reading will encourage exploration of connections between citizen science and political action aimed at conservation of

13

critical habitats. Student groups could read different sections of the article and come together in a jigsaw fashion to share what they have learned. Another option is to ask groups to focus on specific aspects while reading the entire article. For example, one group could focus on the role of citizen scientists in informing conservation action. Another group could focus on the connection between scientific data and community politics, and a third on comparing their work with the work of this other group of citizen scientists.

On the Web

- Citizen Science Central (*www.birds.cornell.edu/citscitoolkit*): A portal for searching citizen science projects by topic and/or location

- SciStarter (*www.scistarter.com*): A portal for searching citizen science projects by topic and/or location

- The Vernal Pool Association (*www.vernalpool.org/vernal_1.htm*): Provides a variety of project ideas and resource materials

- Vermont Vernal Pool Mapping Project (*www.vtecostudies.org/VPMP/training.html*): Includes resources such as field ID cards for vernal pool indicator species and a key to amphibian eggs and larvae

Additional Resources

Kesselheim, A. S., B. E. Slattery, S. Higgins and M. R. Schilling. 1995. *WOW! The wonders of wetlands: An educator's guide*. Bozeman, MT: The Watercourse.
Summary: Provides background material on wetlands and activities ranging from making inexpensive sampling equipment to participating in wetland enhancement and stewardship projects. Includes appendix information on planning and developing a school yard wetland habitat.

Oscarson, D. B., and A. J. K. Calhoun. 2007. Developing vernal pool conservation plans at the local level using citizen-scientists. *Wetlands* 27 (1): 80–95.
Summary: Presents four case studies in which citizen scientists conducted vernal pool field assessments that guided town development of local conservation strategies.

Project WET Foundation. 2011. *Project WET curriculum and activity guide 2.0*. Bozeman, MT: Project WET International Foundation.
Summary: Contains multidisciplinary water-related activities for students. The guide is cross-referenced with planning charts and a glossary.

U.S. Environmental Protection Agency, Office of Water. *Protecting wetlands for amphibian and reptile conservation. EPA 843-F-03-015. http://water.epa.gov/type/wetlands/ outreach/upload/herp-conservation-pr.pdf*
Summary: A fact sheet on the importance of ephemeral wetlands, threats faced by reptiles and amphibians, and recommended conservation strategies.

Using Inland and Coastal Citizen Science Opportunities to Study Marine Food Webs

*by Melissa K. Demetrikopoulos, Lee G. Morris, and Wesley D. Thompson,
Institute for Biomedical Philosophy, Dunedin, FL*

Overview

Students engage in virtual and field-based scientific discovery related to aquatic food webs, learning that all organisms are interconnected and discovering the impact of upstream activities on marine organisms. Even students living far from a coral reef can investigate their local water quality and participate in citizen science relevant to marine food webs.

Objectives

Students will be able to:

- Differentiate a food chain from a food web

- Research organisms in a marine food web and outline food web relationships

- Predict how habitat change might affect organisms in the food web

- Work with authentic data to produce graphs and draw conclusions

Big Idea

Runoff from land even far from the sea carries fertilizers, pesticides, motor oil, and other pollutants that impact both freshwater and marine food webs.

Citizen Science Connection

- REEF (*http://reef.org/db/reports*)

- World Water Monitoring Challenge (*www. worldwatermonitoringday.org/default.aspx*)

Time Required/Location

Three 30–45 minute blocks, which can be conducted independently indoors, plus a field project completed over several days or as an all-day trip, outdoors

LESSON 14
Using Inland and Coastal Citizen Science Opportunities to
Study Marine Food Webs

Resources Needed

- Computer with internet access

- 3 × 5 cards, with a hole punched in each side (3–5 cards per student)

- Colored pencils

- Yarn

- Habitat Food Web Worksheet (1 per student)

Background Information

Organisms in any community are linked through what they eat and what eats them. A food chain is a pathway connecting a producer with several levels of consumers. The feeding relationships in an ecosystem consist of many food chains interconnected into a network called a food web. In most food webs, plants (producers) use sunlight and inorganic materials to produce organic compounds, such as carbohydrates, that are incorporated into the organism and become food and nutrients for other organisms that eat them—the consumers. Scavengers feed on dead organisms, and decomposers break down nonliving organic matter into materials that are released into the environment and become available to reenter the food chain as nutrients.

These basics are true in most marine food webs, where the key producers are phytoplankton. These tiny organisms—such as diatoms and dinoflagellates—are the foundation of the ocean's entire biological community. Most phytoplankton are buoyant and float in the upper part of the ocean, where sunlight penetrates the water. Besides sunlight, phytoplankton require inorganic nutrients such as nitrates; phosphates; and sulfur, which they convert into proteins, fats, and carbohydrates. Phytoplankton become food for zooplankton (very small ocean organisms such as copepods and other grazers), which feed small crustaceans, which feed the stripers and bluefish, which feed larger organisms such as tunas and sharks. In deep sea vents where there is no sunlight, other food webs exist where the producers use chemical energy from deep ocean hydrothermal vents and inorganic materials to produce the organic compounds necessary for life that become food for consumers. Although the producers in these deep sea food webs are quite different from the producers elsewhere, the rest of the food web is similar.

Marine food webs are impacted by what happens on land and in the air. Land-based sources of marine pollution include runoff from farms and urban areas (e.g., fertilizers, pesticides, and motor oil), wind-blown dust, toxic chemicals in industrial and municipal wastewaters, and soil erosion. Potentially toxic chemicals adhere to tiny particles in the ocean and are taken up by phytoplankton, which are eaten by consumers. These toxins are concentrated upward within ocean food webs. When these pesticides and toxic metals are absorbed into the food web, they can cause mutations and diseases throughout the food web, but especially in higher trophic levels. Air pollution also impacts marine food webs due to acid rain that changes the ocean pH (particularly in coastal regions) and reduces biodiversity in these regions. In addition to the effects of toxins and changes in pH, air pollution and runoff from the land impact marine food webs by causing overloading of nitrogen and phosphate nutrients, leading to overgrowth of algae. This blocks sunlight to organisms living at greater depths. Excessive growth of algae, called algae blooms, can lead to large-scale death of fish and other marine organisms due to suffocation because decay of the algae decreases dissolved oxygen. In addition, some algae produce toxins that are released when they die, killing fish and other marine organisms.

Conducting the Activity

Engage

1. Have students work in small groups to develop food webs. Assign each group to work with a specific marine habitat type such as tide pool, estuary, sea grass bed, innertidal zones (which may be rocky, sandy or muddy flats), deep sea vent, or open ocean (pelagic). Alternatively, assign each group to work with a specific marine region (such as Gulf of Mexico, Mediterranean Sea, Atlantic Ocean, Pacific Ocean, Arctic Ocean, or Indian Ocean). Depending on your students and the time allotted to the project, either allow the groups to define where their food webs are located or assign a habitat type or marine region.

2. Ask students to brainstorm and write a list of organisms that live in their specific habitat. Provide punched 3 × 5 cards and invite students to write the name of one organism per card, sketching it on one side and listing its diet and predators on the other side.

3. After students have had time to begin listing organisms, project Tables 14.1 and 14.2 (p. 176) on a screen or write these categories on the board, and prompt students to use them in thinking about additional organisms within their designated habitat. (Note: Some student groups may be able to come up with a seemingly endless list of very specific organisms, which may necessitate a larger number of cards, or you may choose to allow them to group several related organisms on one card.) If students have no prior knowledge

of the habitat, they may list very general terms such as plants and insects. If
necessary, allow them to use the internet or other resources to determine specific organisms within their habitat.

*Table 14.3 shows an example set of organisms for an Intertidal Zone
food web.*

TABLE 14.1.

Organisms in the Food Web by Classification

I. Plants	II. Animals	III. Fungi	IV. Protists	V. Bacteria*

A. Flowering
B. Cone Bearing
C. Mosses
D. Ferns
	A. Invertebrates
	  1. Sponges
	  2. Worms
	  3. Mollusks
	  4. Echinoderms
	  5. Arthropods
	    a. Crabs
	    b. Spiders
	    c. Insects			

	B. Vertebrates
	  1. Fish
	  2. Amphibians
	  3. Reptiles
	  4. Birds
	  5. Mammals			

*Bacteria represent two kingdoms (Archaebacteria and Eubacteria)

TABLE 14.2.

Organisms in the Food Web by Diet

Herbivores	Carnivores	Omnivores	Scavengers	Decomposers

TABLE 14.3.

Example Food Web Information for the Intertidal Zone (Section of Beach Exposed and Covered During Tidal Change)

Organism	Diet (What does it consume or derive energy from?)	Predators (What eats it?)
Sea grass	sunlight	periwinkle snails, sea urchin
Seaweed	sunlight	sea urchins, bait fish
Phytoplankton	sunlight	clams, barnacles, oyster, sea anemone, bait fish
Zooplankton	organic debris, other plankton	clams, barnacles, oyster, sea anemone, bait fish
Algae	sunlight	parrot fish
Barnacles	plankton	sheepshead fish
Clams	plankton	starfish, sheepshead fish
Periwinkle snails	algae, sea grass	gulls, cranes, starfish
Conchs	algae, conchs	starfish, sting rays
Starfish	sea anemone, clams	sting rays
Shrimp	algae, dead organisms	gulls
Blue crabs	almost everything, dead or alive	red drum, stingray, gulls, egrets, cranes, osprey, raccoons
Fiddler crabs	algae, plankton	gulls, egrets, cranes, sheepshead fish
Stone crabs	clams, snails, conchs	conch, sting rays
Sea urchin	sea grass, algae, seaweed	gulls, sting rays
Sea anemone	plankton	starfish
Sting ray	starfish, blue crabs	(nothing likely to be in the intertidal zone)
Bait fish (menhaden, shad, sardines, mullet, pinfish)	shrimp, blue crabs, algae, seaweed, plankton	gulls, cranes, osprey
Red drum	blue crabs, baitfish	osprey, sea gulls
Parrot fish	algae, sea grass	osprey
Sheepshead fish	barnacles, clams, fiddler crabs	osprey
Seagulls	blue crabs, snails, shrimp	(nothing likely to be in the intertidal zone)
Cranes	blue crabs, shrimp	(nothing likely to be in the intertidal zone)
Osprey	fish	(nothing likely to be in the intertidal zone)
Raccoons	crabs, clams, snails, shrimp	(nothing likely to be in the intertidal zone)

14

4. Have each group produce a food web by attaching their cards with yarn,
    connecting each organism to its predators and prey. Each web should also
    include a card identifying the energy source—either the Sun or hydrother-
    mal chemicals. As students add their cards to the web, encourage them to
    make as many connections as possible and discuss with each other why each
    connection is made.

Explore

1. Invite students to take part in a fish count at the Coral Reef Fish Count
    website, where they can identify fish that live on the coral reefs of St. Ann's
    Bay in Jamaica (*http://warrensburg.k12.mo.us/coral/coral.html*). Using informa-
    tion provided about the diet of these fish, ask students to construct a food
    web for this habitat. The site provides data sheets and answer keys for the
    identification.

2. If your school lies in a coastal area, your classes could participate in an
    actual fish count. The REEF project provides webinars useful in preparing
    for fish counts (*www.reef.org/resources/webinars*) and a place to submit and
    explore fish count data (*www.reef.org/db/reports*).

Explain

1. Using examples from the data analysis section of the Coral Reef Fish Count
    site (located at the conclusion of the virtual fish count (*http://warrensburg.
    k12.mo.us/coral/coral.html*), discuss the various ways in which the data can be
    explored mathematically and represented graphically. Ask students to pose
    a question and then select which method is most suitable for analyzing and
    portraying the results with that particular question in mind.

    *For example, if they want to know what percentage of the fish
    are herbivores, it may be most appropriate to represent the diet
    of the fish using a pie chart. However, if they want to know how
    many of the fish are herbivores, it may be most appropriate to
    represent the diet of the fish using a bar graph.*

2. Encourage students to research the fish that they found virtually or in the
    field. FishBase (*www.fishbase.org*) is a useful source of information about
    specific species.

3. Remind students of trophic levels (Table 14.4) and introduce relevant new vocabulary (Table 14.5, p. 180). Ask them to create a food web containing one or more of the fish species they have observed.

TABLE 14.4.

Organisms in the Food Web by Trophic Levels

Producers (Autotrophs)	Primary Consumers	Secondary Consumers	Tertiary Consumers	Scavengers/ Decomposers
• Make their own food • May use solar energy (photosynthesis) (e.g., plants and phytoplankton) • May use chemical energy from deep ocean hydro-thermal vents (chemosynthesis)	• Eat producers (zooplankton, herbivores and omnivores) • May eat bacteria involved in chemosynthesis • May also be parasites	• Eat primary consumers (carnivores insectivores and omnivores) • May also be parasites	• Eat secondary consumers (carnivores that eat carnivores) • Note: Quaternary consumers eat tertiary consumers and so on	• Scavengers (detrivores) eat dead organisms (vultures, crabs, maggots) • Decomposers (saprophytes) convert dead organisms back to basic compounds and elements (bacteria, fungus)

Elaborate

1. Use NASA's Earth Observatory site (*www.earthobservatory.nasa.gov/Experiments/ CitizenScientist/WaterQuality*) to help students understand the importance of citizen science in monitoring the physical, chemical, and biological characteristics of water. You could liken this monitoring to visiting your doctor for periodic checkups. NASA's site provides useful background information about the relationships between freshwater and marine water quality, aquatic food webs, and human quality of life. By contributing water-monitoring data from inland sites, students can help scientists track the effects of fertilizer and other nutrient sources on blooms of algae in the ocean.

    Algae form the base of the food web in most marine systems, but too much algal growth can be destructive (see Background Information). In coastal areas, problematic algal blooms are closely linked to nutrient loading of phosphates and nitrogen from the watersheds feeding into these ocean systems.

TABLE 14.5.

Key Vocabulary

Term	Definition
Autotrophs	Organisms that make their own food from inorganic sources such as light energy or chemical energy: (also called producers)
Heterotrophs	Organisms that eat other organisms or organic matter and cannot make their food from inorganic sources (also called consumers)
Photosynthesis	Process whereby plants and some algae use light energy from the Sun to make food
Chemosynthesis	Process whereby microbes such as bacteria and fungi use chemical energy from inorganic compounds to make food
Phytoplankton	Microscopic organisms that live in the ocean and use photosynthesis to make food
Zooplankton	Microscopic organisms that live in the ocean and eat other plankton and organic debris
Herbivores	Organisms that eat plants
Carnivores	Organisms that eat animals
Insectivores	Carnivores that each insects
Piscivores	Carnivores that eat fish
Omnivores	Organisms that eat plants and animals
Parasites	Organisms that live off another organism and harm it while doing so
Top predators	Organisms that have few natural enemies (but can have parasites)
Detritivores	Organisms that eat dead plants or animals (also called scavengers)
Saprophytes	Organisms that live on dead or decaying plants or animals (also called decomposers)
Pelagic	Area of the ocean that is neither near the shore nor near the bottom (also called open ocean or water column)
Food chain	A path indicating which organism eats the next in an ecosystem that starts with an energy source and concludes with top predators
Food web	A network illustrating interconnections among organisms within an ecosystem and demonstrating that organisms may be a part of several food chains and at different trophic levels within the same food web.
Trophic level	The position that an organism occupies in a food chain and a measure of distance from the primary producers which are at the base of each chain
Nutrient loading	Increase in nutrients such as nitrogen and phosphates to aquatic environments due to runoff from the land or precipitation from the air
Watershed	The area of land that drains to a specific body of water

Ask students, "What is citizen science?"

> ***Citizen science*** *refers to efforts in which volunteers partner with professional scientists to collect or analyze data. Citizen science water monitoring efforts are used to raise public awareness and to support the protection of water bodies and the life they support. Fish survey data are used by agencies and nonprofits to guide reef management decisions. Students can read current and past scientific and monitoring reports at* http://reef.org/programs/monitoring. *See Chapter 1, "What Is Citizen Science?" for more information.*

2. Consider participating in the World Water Monitoring Challenge, a well-organized way in which students worldwide can conduct field-based exploration of their local water quality and share their results online (*www.worldwatermonitoringday.org*).

Evaluate

1. Have students complete the Habitat Food Web Worksheet using the habitat they worked on in the Engage section and then draw a food web diagram showing the interconnects and write a brief essay explaining the connections among organisms in that habitat. Rubrics for evaluating the student presentations can be found at *http://energeticeinsteins.com/uploads/Rubrics_for_Food_Web_Section_in.pdf*

2. Graphs created by students in the Explain step could be used to assess their ability to produce appropriate graphs and draw defensible conclusions.

Extend

1. Have students develop a food web of the organisms in their school yard or backyard and upload digital images of organisms into a citizen science site such as Wildlife Watch (*www.nwf.org/wildlifewatch*) or Wildlife Sightings (*www.wildlifesightings.net*).

2. Another option is to design an experiment to look into human impacts. For example, students could investigate the impact of a disturbed environment on biodiversity and food webs by counting the number of species found along a transect, for example close to a roadside versus farther away, or in

14

a marina versus in a less disturbed section of shoreline. They could explore the number of links and the number of levels of the food webs.

They are likely to find that disturbed areas have decreased biodiversity and less extensive food webs compared with more pristine areas.

Lesson Resource

- Habitat Food Web Worksheet

Habitat Food Web Worksheet

14

Habitat type: _____

1. Place each organism into the chart according to its diet and trophic level(s). An organism may fit into more than one trophic level, depending on its food web relationships.

Diet	Trophic Level				
	Producer (autotroph)	Primary Consumer	Secondary Consumer	Tertiary Consumer	Scavenger/ Decomposer
1. Sunlight or chemical energy					
2. Plants					
3. Animals					
3a. Insects					
3b. Fish					
4. Plants and animals					
5. Dead organic matter					

2. Describe two potential habitat changes and explain how these might affect food webs in that type of habitat.

Tree Squirrels

Narrators of Nature in Your Neighborhood

by Steve Sullivan, Kristi Backe, and Michelle Rabkin, Chicago Academy of Sciences

Overview

Students observe and record wildlife behavior while conducting experiments and analyzing data to determine how squirrels perceive the safety of various foraging locations. Squirrels make good study organisms because they are easy to find and respond to environmental conditions that similarly influence the behavior of other forms of wildlife.

Learning Objectives

Students will be able to:

- Predict which school yard locations are likely to be preferred foraging locations for tree squirrels

- Compare and contrast squirrel foraging behaviors and measure food consumption at locations with different environmental conditions

- Evaluate feeding at multiple locations to test hypotheses about squirrel behavior

Big Idea

Wildlife feeding and foraging behavior depends on a number of factors, including the perceived safety of an animal's surroundings.

Citizen Science Connection

- Project Squirrel (*www.projectsquirrel.org*)

Time Required/Location

Ten 30-minute class periods, indoors and outdoors. This includes:

- Three 30-minute periods for introduction, experiment setup, and initial general site observations

- Four 30-minute periods for measuring and recording data (four consecutive days)

- Two 30-minute periods for data analysis

- One 30-minute period to elaborate and evaluate

Resources Needed

- Computer with internet access

- Projector or interactive whiteboard

- Photos, grey and fox squirrels

- Outdoor space with trees and squirrels present

- 2 measuring tapes

- Calculator

- 16 ears of feed corn (4 ears per day; minimum of 4 days)

- Balance (300 g capacity)

- 16 one-gallon resealable bags (4 bags per day; minimum of 4 days)

- Permanent marker

- Graph paper (1 per student)

- Clipboards

- Corn Data Collection Sheet (4 per student; 1 per day; minimum of 4 days)

- Data Analysis Sheet (1 per student)

- Downloads from *www.projectsquirrel.org*:

  o Habitat Information Sheet (1 per group)

  o Class Data Sheet transparency (or file to display with a projector)

  o Project Squirrel Reporting Sheet

- 4 cardboard foraging patches, each assembled from the following materials (see Foraging Patch Assembly Instructions at www.projectsquirrel.org):

  o Cardboard square: 60 cm × 60 cm piece

  o 6 × ¼ in. screw eye or hooked wire stake

  o 1 in. screw eye

  o 10 cm piece of wire

  o Duct tape

  o Utility knife or box cutter

  o 1 coarse-thread screw eye, 1 in. or longer

Background Information

Project Squirrel explores feeding behaviors of North American squirrels. Heavier foraging occurs in places considered relatively safe from potential predators or other dangers. When, where, and the extent to which an animal forages for food therefore reveals a lot about how that individual perceives its environment.

A corn kernel has two main parts: the endosperm (the starchy outside) and the embryo (the oily inside) (Figure 15.1). When corn germinates, the growing embryo is fed by the endosperm until the plant forms leaves and begins to photosynthesize.

Squirrels often eat only the nutrient-rich embryo, leaving the endosperm behind (Figure 15.2). Sometimes, squirrels will eat very quickly and leave a pile of broken corn kernel scraps behind instead of leaving a kernel with the embryo neatly cut out. In this lesson, students record the amount of corn and scraps remaining at each site after foraging and then calculate estimates of the amounts consumed.

Additional background information is available on the Project Squirrel website.

FIGURE 15.1.

The embryo and endosperm in a corn kernel

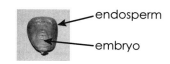

FIGURE 15.2.

Corn kernels with only endosperm remaining after squirrels have excised and eaten the embryos

Conducting the Activity

Engage

1. Ask students to generate a list of animals they have observed in the school yard, and record the list on the board. If squirrels are not mentioned, ask if students have seen them. Invite students to share their observations of squirrel behavior.

2. Using photos from the Project Squirrel website, introduce students to grey and fox squirrels, the two most common tree squirrel species in the United States. Introduce the distinguishing characteristics (belly color and tail

markings) and quiz students informally to ensure that they can distinguish them.

3. Take students outside and give them a few minutes to look at the school yard and imagine it from the perspective of a squirrel. Ask them to create a sketch showing areas that seem relatively safe for squirrels and others that seem less safe, and explain their reasoning.

4. Return inside, and explain that scientists are interested in how animals behave in areas where they feel safe or threatened. One way to test this is to provide food in various locations and then measure how much has been eaten. Ask:

   - What might you expect to observe if you put food in an area of the school yard that seems safe for squirrels?

   - How might this differ if you provide food in a place that seems relatively unsafe for squirrels?

   - In which type of location would squirrels be likely to eat more food?

   If necessary, present an analogy of a person's response to food in places that seem safe or dangerous. For example, have students imagine they have access to a bowl of candy on the kitchen table and another in the middle of a busy street. Would they eat the same amount of candy from each bowl?

5. Inform students that scientists are addressing these same questions about squirrel behavior and have formed hypotheses about how the relative safety of a location impacts the quantity of food consumed by squirrels. Introduce Project Squirrel by visiting the website or discussing what kinds of data this project accepts from citizen scientists. Highlight the importance of the volunteers by explaining that scientists can't be in every city gathering data throughout the year and therefore rely on citizen scientist help. Explain that the class will look at food consumption to help scientists learn about influences of environmental conditions on the behavior of wildlife.

Explore

1. Explain that in order for citizen science data to be compiled into a data set useful for research, participants must follow standardized procedures. In Project Squirrel, these include:

- Selecting a "Safe" and an "Unsafe" site, taking into account that both types of sites will need to include a tree.

- Placing two foraging patches at each site, one at the base of a tree and another 4 m from the tree, with all foraging patches placed at least 4 m from any other trees, fences, walls, or buildings.

- Installing an ear of corn at each foraging patch on four consecutive days and recording how much has been consumed by the end of the day in each location.

Note: You will place the foraging patches in the school yard in the locations selected by the students each morning on the four data collection days. The patches should be out in the school yard for a minimum of six hours and should not be left out overnight. You will need to collect the corn and patches at the end of each day. The Foraging Patch Assembly Instruction sheet explains how to assemble patches, attach corn, and collect at the end of each day. As much as possible, place the patches in the school yard on four consecutive days with similar weather forecasts. If necessary, postpone a day of data collection if the weather forecast is drastically different from the other days of data collection.

2. Divide students into four groups, and assign each group a foraging patch to investigate:

   - Safe Site Near Tree

   - Safe Site 4 m from Tree

   - Unsafe Site Near Tree, and

   - Unsafe Site 4 m from Tree

3. Go outside and finalize selection of Safe and Unsafe site locations. As a class or in two groups, fill out one Habitat Information Sheet for the Safe site and another for the Unsafe site.

4. Back inside, provide each group with a Data Collection Sheet and a cob of feed corn. Students should circle their site (Safe or Unsafe) and foraging patch (Near Tree or 4 m from Tree) and mark that this Data Collection Sheet is for Day 1 of data collection. Have each group use a balance to find the initial mass of their corncob (to the nearest gram) and record this value on

the Data Collection Sheet. The group should then place their corncob in a resealable bag labeled with the group's name and the day of data collection (e.g., "Safe Site Near Tree, Day 1"). Give students time to fill out Data Collection Sheets and prepare corncobs for Days 2–4.

5. Early each day of data collection, place the foraging patches in the appropriate locations.

6. At some point during the day, have students count how many and what kinds of squirrels they see in or near their designated Safe or Unsafe site over a 5-minute interval and add it to that day's Data Collection Sheet. To avoid disturbing the squirrels, ask them to observe from inside or sit quietly at a distance from the foraging sites.

7. After the foraging patches have been out for at least six hours, collect the remaining corn from the foraging patches, place in labeled bags (according to the directions in the Foraging Patch Assembly Instructions), and bring the foraging patches inside.

8. Give each group the bag of corn collected from their foraging patch. Introduce and show pictures of "whole kernels," "kernels with excised embryos," and "small pieces of kernels." Explain how to fill out the rest of the Data Collection Sheet:

   - Remove the whole kernels from the cob.

   - Separate the corn into piles according to the categories listed above.

   - Weigh each pile and the empty cob, and record the data.

   - Calculate the mass of corn kernel scraps:

Corn kernel scraps	=	Mass of kernels with excised embryos	+	Mass of small pieces of embryos

Note: The mass of "corn kernel scraps" indicates how much is left behind after squirrels have consumed the more nutritious part of the kernels.

   - Calculate how much corn was consumed:

Corn consumed	=	initial mass of corn before foraging	–	Mass of cob with all kernels removed	–	Mass of whole kernels left behind by squirrels

9. Repeat the procedure each day by placing foraging patches in the same locations, conducting 5-minute observations, bringing in the patches at the end of the day, and filling out a new Data Collection Sheet.

10. After four days of data collection, calculate the average mass of corn kernel scraps and of corn consumed at each foraging patch location over the four days. Use the Class Data Sheet to compile and average the data collected by all four groups.

11. Pass out a Data Analysis Sheet and graph paper to each student. Ask them to create two bar graphs to present the data at the four locations, using the means calculated on the Class Data Sheet. One graph should depict the average mass of corn kernel scraps left behind in each foraging patch, and the other the average mass of corn consumed in each patch.

12. Have students analyze the class data in their graphs and respond to the questions on the Data Analysis Sheet.

To help students analyze data, you may wish to clarify that the two data calculations compiled on the Class Data Sheet provide two different ways of looking at how much corn the squirrels were interested in eating. Because squirrels don't eat the whole corn kernel, they leave behind clues about how much they actually ate. Compare the corn kernel scraps left behind on the foraging patch to candy wrappers. If we put out a bowl of candy and look at the wrappers left behind, we can figure out approximately how much candy was eaten at a given location. When we measure the corn kernel scraps, we are doing the same thing with the squirrels. The corn consumed calculation, however, tells us how much corn is actually missing from the foraging patch. This calculation takes the starting mass of the cob (including kernels) and subtracts all whole kernels of corn left behind in order to calculate how much is missing. Both calculations estimate how much corn the squirrels ate.

Explain

As a class, discuss students' conclusions about which location seems safest to squirrels:

• What factors can students identify that may have impacted the amount of food consumed by the squirrels?

- How does this compare with their initial ideas about features that might make a location seem safe or unsafe?

- What conclusions can students draw about squirrels' willingness to venture away from trees in search of food? What data support these conclusions?

- Do the data from both graphs suggest the same site as safest? If not, what factors might be contributing to the differences? If so, what features of each site do students think are most important?

Elaborate

Place students in pairs or small groups. Explain that each group will conclude where they think the ideal squirrel habitat is located in the school yard based on their data collection and analysis.

- Give students time to discuss their ideas in their pairs or small groups, and have each group present their ideas to the class. Encourage students to use data to support their choices.

- To highlight the collaborative nature of science and the importance placed on questioning the ideas of others, encourage students to constructively share their doubts about other groups' claims. Are there alternate explanations backed by data that the group may have overlooked?

- Remind students that their data will be useful to Project Squirrel scientists in their studies of the habitat preferences of squirrels throughout the country. Compile the class data and submit a single report to Project Squirrel.

Evaluate

1. Student presentations in the Elaborate section can be used to assess their achievement of the learning objectives.

2. Assess students' ability to analyze similar situations and provide thoughtful responses about what behavior they would expect from squirrels. For example, sketch a simple map showing several trees and corn foraging patches. Place one patch near a busy road, another near a residential street where cats roam and people walk their dogs, and the third in the middle of the ground in between. Ask students to mark where they would expect squirrels to consume the least corn and the most corn, and to support their answers based on evidence from their own research.

Extend

1. To more closely monitor foraging behavior at the four foraging patches, have one or two students observe each site once per hour and record and share their observations.

2. Set up an investigation similar to the school yard experiment to study foraging behaviors of squirrels in other locations or to study the foraging behaviors of another species. If students are testing other squirrel foraging locations, they may wish to use the same experimental design. If they wish to investigate foraging behavior of animals other than squirrels, they will first need to research the eating behaviors of that type of animal to determine what type of food to provide and how and where it should be presented (on the ground, above ground, on a platform, covered or uncovered, and so on). Compare conclusions with those from the original squirrel investigation.

Lesson Resources

- Corn Data Collection Sheet

- Data Analysis Sheet

On the Web

- Project Squirrel (*www.projectsquirrel.org*): A citizen science project that explores the feeding behaviors of North American squirrels.

Reference

Sullivan, S. M. 2011. *Project squirrel citizen science research guide*. Chicago: Chicago Academy of Sciences.

15

Corn Data Collection Sheet

Investigator Names: _____

Hypothesized Habitat Type: (circle one)   Safe   Unsafe

Foraging Patch Location: (circle one)   Near Tree   4 m from Tree

Date: _____   Day # _____ of data collection

Time patch opened: _____ a.m./p.m.   Time patch closed: _____ a.m./p.m.

Squirrel species observed in the schoolyard today:

☐   Grey Squirrel *Sciurus carolinensis* Number_____

☐   Fox Squirrel *Sciurus niger*   Number_____

☐   Other _____ Number_____

Mass of corncob (before foraging): _____ g

Has feeding occurred today? (circle one)   Yes / No

If yes, use the corncob and all corn kernels (whole or in pieces) collected from the cardboard foraging patch to continue:

1.   Set the corncob to the side. Do not remove any kernels from the cob at this time.

2.   Split the remaining corn into three piles:

      whole kernels   kernels with excised embryos   small pieces of kernels

3.   Kernels with excised embryos and small pieces of kernels are the scraps of kernels that were nibbled on by squirrels. Find the masses of these two piles, and use them to calculate the total mass of corn kernel scraps left behind on the foraging patch:

Mass of kernels with excised embryos (not on the cob):	+	Mass of small pieces of kernels (not on the cob):	=	Total mass of corn kernel scraps left behind on foraging patch:
g		g		g

4. The squirrels may also have left behind kernels that are still whole, either attached to the cob or loose on the foraging patch. Remove the whole kernels from the cob and combine them with the pile of whole kernels that were loose on the foraging patch (already set aside during step 2).

5. Find the mass of this new pile that is made up of all of the whole corn kernels left behind by squirrels, either loose on the foraging patch or removed from the cob by you.

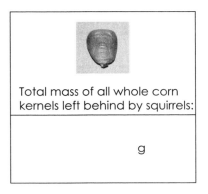

Total mass of all whole corn kernels left behind by squirrels:

_____ g

6. Find the mass of the cob (with all kernels removed): _____ g

Use the data collected to determine the mass of all corn that was consumed by squirrels:

Initial mass of corn – mass of empty cob – mass of whole kernels left behind =

Mass of corn consumed by squirrels: _____g

Data Analysis Sheet

Name:_____

1. Use the graphs you created to compare squirrel feeding behavior in the safe location and the unsafe location. In which location was more corn consumed? In which location did the squirrels leave behind more scraps? Explain.

2. Use the graphs you created to compare squirrel feeding behavior near a tree and 4 m from a tree. In each location (safe; unsafe), where was more corn consumed, near the tree or 4m from the tree? What differences do you notice in the amount of scraps the squirrels left behind near the tree and 4 m from the tree?

3. Based on the data collected, are your hypotheses about the relative safety of each location supported or refuted? Explain.

4. Are there any interesting data that were surprising? Explain. How do the "corn consumed" data compare to the "corn kernel scraps" data? Do the graphs look similar?

Appendix 1
Lessons Mapped to Scientific Practices*

Lesson #	Lesson Topic	Asking questions and defining problems	Developing and using models	Planning and carrying out investigations	Analyzing and interpreting data	Using mathematics and computational thinking	Constructing explanations and designing solutions	Engaging in argument from evidence	Obtaining, evaluating, and communicating information
1	Whale Song	X			X				X
2	Monarch Butterflies				X	X	X	X	
3	Soil Invertebrates	X		X	X	X	X	X	X
4	Earthworms	X		X	X		X	X	X
5	Animated Bird Maps	X	X		X	X	X	X	X
6	Bird Migration	X	X		X		X	X	X
7	Wildlife Habitat	X	X	X	X	X	X	X	X
8	Winter Twigs	X		X	X				X
9	Plant Phenology	X			X		X	X	X
10	Ozone Bio-monitoring	X		X	X	X	X	X	X
11	Turtles	X		X	X		X	X	X
12	Frogs and Toads	X		X		X	X	X	X
13	Wetlands	X		X	X		X	X	X
14	Marine Food Webs	X	X	X	X	X	X	X	X
15	Squirrels	X		X	X	X	X	X	X

* Identified in the *Next Generation Science Standards* and *A Framework for K–12 Science Education*.

Achieve Inc. 2013. *Next generation science standards. www.nextgenscience.org/next-generation-science-standards*

National Research Council (NRC). 2012. *A framework for K–12 science education: Practices, crosscutting concepts, and core ideas*. Washington, DC: National Academies Press.

Appendix 2

Lessons Mapped to Crosscutting Concepts*

Lesson #	Lesson Topic	Patterns	Cause and Effect	Scale, Proportion, and Quantity	Systems and System Models	Energy and Matter	Structure and Function	Stability and Change
1	Whale Song	X	X		X			X
2	Monarch Butterflies	X		X				
3	Soil Invertebrates	X	X		X			X
4	Earthworms	X	X		X		X	X
5	Animated Bird Maps	X	X		X			X
6	Bird Migration	X	X		X			X
7	Wildlife Habitat	X	X	X	X			
8	Winter Twigs	X		X	X		X	X
9	Plant Phenology	X	X	X	X	X	X	X
10	Ozone Bio-monitoring	X	X	X	X			X
11	Turtles	X	X		X		X	
12	Frogs and Toads	X	X		X		X	X
13	Wetlands	X	X		X	X	X	X
14	Marine Food Webs	X	X		X	X		X
15	Squirrels	X	X		X			X

* Identified in the *Next Generation Science Standards* and *A Framework for K–12 Science Education*.

Achieve Inc. 2013. N*ext generation science standards. www.nextgenscience.org/next-generation-science-standards*

National Research Council (NRC). 2012. *A framework for K–12 science education: Practices, crosscutting concepts, and core ideas.* Washington, DC: National Academies Press.

The crosscutting concepts for K–12 science classrooms are:

1. Patterns (Noticing repeating events; describing relationships; classifying objects based on careful observations; organizing data in ways that makes pattern recognition more apparent)

2. Cause and effect: Mechanism and explanation (Explaining causal relationships using evidence)

3. Scale, proportion, and quantity (Recognizing that the way things work may change with scale; thinking in terms of magnitude)

4. Systems and system models (Acknowledging boundaries, components, resources and flow within and across systems; interdependence within systems; models of systems including the assumptions and limitations associated with the model)

5. Energy and matter: Flows, cycles, and conservation (Explaining how energy and matter transfer in and out of a system)

6. Structure and function (Exploring the relationship between structure and function at many different levels)

7. Stability and change (Understanding how change occurs in nature)

Appendix 3
Lessons Mapped to Key Science Topics

Lesson #	Lesson Topic	Habitat	Life Cycles	Adaptation	Migration	Biological Interdependence	Biotic/Abiotic Interdependence	Communication	Climate Change	Growth & Development of Organisms	Ecosystem Dynamics	Biodiversity	Conservation	Wetlands	Human Impacts	Food Webs	Animal Behavior
1	Whale Song							X					X		X		X
2	Monarch Butterflies				X				X	X							
3	Soil Invertebrates	X				X	X		X			X					
4	Earthworms	X		X	X		X		X		X						X
5	Animated Bird Maps	X	X		X		X				X						X
6	Bird Migration	X	X		X	X	X		X		X		X		X		X
7	Wildlife Habitat	X				X	X						X		X		
8	Winter Twigs	X	X				X		X	X							
9	Plant Phenology	X	X	X		X	X		X		X	X			X	X	X
10	Ozone Bio-monitoring	X					X				X	X			X		
11	Turtles	X				X	X						X		X		
12	Frogs and Toads	X	X			X	X	X	X			X	X	X	X		X
13	Wetlands	X	X	X	X	X	X				X	X	X	X	X		
14	Marine Food Webs	X	X	X		X	X				X	X	X		X	X	
15	Squirrels	X				X	X				X						X

Appendix 4
Lessons Mapped to Science Process Skills

Lesson #	Lesson Topic	Making observations	Generating questions	Turning questions into hypotheses	Collecting data	Representing and interpreting data and graphs	Collaborating	Sharing Results	Understanding scientific models	Using and understanding maps
1	Whale Song	X				X	X	X		
2	Monarch Butterflies					X	X			X
3	Soil Invertebrates	X	X		X	X	X	X		
4	Earthworms	X	X		X	X	X	X		X
5	Animated Bird Maps	X	X	X		X	X	X	X	X
6	Bird Migration		X			X	X	X	X	X
7	Wildlife Habitat	X			X		X	X	X	X
8	Winter Twigs	X	X		X			X		
9	Plant Phenology	X			X	X	X	X		
10	Ozone Bio-monitoring	X			X		X			
11	Turtles	X	X		X		X	X		
12	Frogs and Toads	X	X		X		X	X		X
13	Wetlands	X	X		X	X	X	X	X	X
14	Marine Food Webs				X	X	X	X		
15	Squirrels	X	X	X	X	X	X	X		X

Appendix 5
Lessons Mapped to Primary Location and Season

Lesson #	Lesson Topic	Primary Location			Season		
		Indoors	In school-yard, garden, or park	Near a pond, wetland, or stream	Fall	Winter	Spring
1	Whale Song	X			X	X	X
2	Monarch Butterflies	X			X	X	X
3	Soil Invertebrates		X		X		X
4	Earthworms	X				X	X
5	Animated Bird Maps	X			X	X	X
6	Bird Migration	X			X	X	X
7	Wildlife Habitat		X		X		X
8	Winter Twigs		X			X	X
9	Plant Phenology		X				X
10	Ozone Bio-monitoring		X		X		X
11	Turtles			X	X		X
12	Frogs and Toads			X		X*	X
13	Wetlands			X		X*	X
14	Marine Food Webs			X	X		X
15	Squirrels		X		X	X	X

* In southern states

Index